A-Level Year 1 & AS

Physics

Exam Board: Edexcel

Revising for Physics exams is stressful, that's for sure — even just getting your notes sorted out can leave you needing a lie down. But help is at hand...

This brilliant CGP book explains **everything you'll need to learn** (and nothing you won't), all in a straightforward style that's easy to get your head around. We've also included **exam questions** to test how ready you are for the real thing.

There's even a free Online Edition you can read on your computer or tablet!

How to get your free Online Edition

Go to **cgpbooks.co.uk/extras** and enter this code...

3037 0066 5657 7645

This code only works for one person. If somebody else has used this book before you, they might have already claimed the Online Edition.

A-Level revision? It has to be CGP!

201686453

Published by CGP

Editors:
Emily Garrett, David Maliphant, Rachael Marshall, Sam Pilgrim, Charlotte Whiteley and Sarah Williams.

Contributors:
Tony Alldridge, Jane Cartwright, Peter Clarke, Barbara Mascetti, John Myers and Andy Williams.

ISBN: 978 1 78294 293 1

With thanks to Mark A. Edwards for the proofreading.
With thanks to Jan Greenway for the copyright research.

www.cgpbooks.co.uk

Clipart from Corel®
Printed by Elanders Ltd, Newcastle upon Tyne.

Based on the classic CGP style created by Richard Parsons.

Contents

The Scientific Process

You'll need the skills covered in Topic 1 throughout your course, so make sure you're clear on everything that comes up on the next 12 pages, and can apply it to the physics you meet in the rest of your AS or A-level.

Scientists Come Up with **Theories** — Then **Test Them**...

Science tries to explain **how** and **why** things happen — it **answers questions**. It's all about seeking and gaining **knowledge** about the world around us. Scientists do this by **asking** questions, **suggesting** answers and then **testing** their suggestions to see if they're correct — this is the **scientific process**.

1) **Ask** a question about **why** something happens or **how** something works. E.g. what is the nature of light?

2) **Suggest** an answer, or part of an answer, by forming a **theory** (a possible **explanation** of the observations) — e.g. light is a wave. (Scientists also sometimes form a **model** too — a **simplified picture** of what's physically going on.)

3) Make a **prediction** or hypothesis — a **specific testable statement**, based on the theory, about what will happen in a test situation. For example, if light is a wave, it will interfere and diffract when it travels through a small enough gap.

4) Carry out a **test** — to provide **evidence** that will support the prediction (or help to disprove it). E.g. shining light through a diffraction grating to show diffraction and interference (p.84).

The evidence supported Quentin's Theory of Flammable Burps.

A theory is only scientific if it can be tested.

...Then They **Tell** Everyone About Their **Results**...

The results are **published** — scientists need to let others know about their work. Scientists publish their results as reports (similar to the lab write-ups you do in school) written up in **scientific journals**. Scientific journals are just like normal magazines, only they contain **scientific reports** (called papers) instead of the latest celebrity gossip.

1) It's important that the **integrity** (trustworthiness) of the reports published in scientific journals is checked. Scientists (like anyone else) might be **dishonest** or **biased**, or an investigation might have made **invalid** conclusions (see page 13).

2) The report is sent out to **peers** — other scientists that are experts in the **same area**. They examine the data and results, and if they think that the conclusion is reasonable it's **published**. This makes sure that work published in scientific journals is of a **good standard**. This process is known as **peer review**.

3) But peer review **can't guarantee** the science is **correct** — other scientists still need to **reproduce** it.

4) Sometimes **mistakes** are made and bad work is published. Peer review **isn't perfect** but it's probably the best way for scientists to self-regulate their work and to publish **quality reports**.

...Then **Other Scientists** Will **Test** the Theory Too

Other scientists read the published theories and results, and try to **test the theory** themselves. This involves:
- Repeating the **exact same experiments**.
- Using the theory to make **new predictions** and then testing them with **new experiments**.

If the **Evidence** Supports a Theory, It's **Accepted** — for Now

1) If all the experiments in all the world provide good evidence to back it up, the theory is thought of as **scientific 'fact'** (for now).

2) But it will never become **totally indisputable** fact. Scientific **breakthroughs or advances** could provide new ways to question and test the theory, which could lead to **new evidence** that **conflicts** with the current evidence. Then the testing starts all over again...

And this, my friend, is the **tentative nature of scientific knowledge** — it's always **changing** and **evolving**.

The Scientific Process

So scientists need evidence to back up their theories. They get it by carrying out experiments, and when that's not possible they carry out studies.

Evidence Comes From Controlled Lab Experiments...

1) Results from **controlled experiments** in **laboratories** are **great**.
2) A lab is the easiest place to **control variables** so that they're all **kept constant** (except for the one you're investigating).

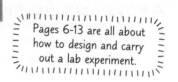
Pages 6-13 are all about how to design and carry out a lab experiment.

...That You can Draw Meaningful Conclusions From

1) You always need to make your experiments as **controlled** as possible so you can be confident that any effects you see are linked to the variable you're changing.
2) If you do find a relationship, you need to be careful what you conclude. You need to decide whether the effect you're seeing is **caused** by changing a variable (this is known as a **causal relationship**), or whether the two are just **correlated**. There's more about drawing conclusions on page 13.

Society Makes Decisions Based on Scientific Evidence

1) Lots of scientific work eventually leads to **important discoveries** or breakthroughs that could **benefit humankind**.
2) These results are **used by society** (that's you, me and everyone else) to **make decisions** — about the way we live, what we eat, what we drive, etc.
3) All sections of society use scientific evidence to make decisions, e.g. politicians use it to devise policies and individuals use science to make decisions about their own lives.

Other factors can **influence** decisions about science or the way science is used:

1) **Economic factors:**
   Society has to consider the **cost** of implementing changes based on scientific conclusions — e.g. the cost of reducing the UK's carbon emissions to limit the human contribution to **climate change**.
   Scientific research is often **expensive**. E.g. in areas such as astronomy, the Government has to **justify** spending money on a new telescope rather than pumping money into, say, the **NHS** or **schools**.

2) **Social factors:**
   Decisions affect **people's lives** — e.g. when looking for a site to build a **nuclear power station**, you need to consider how it would affect the lives of the people in the **surrounding area**.

3) **Environmental factors:**
   Many scientists suggest that building **wind farms** would be a **cheap** and **environmentally friendly** way to generate electricity in the future. But some people think that because **wind turbines** can **harm wildlife** such as birds and bats, other methods of generating electricity should be used.

Practice Questions

Q1 What is peer review?
Q2 Explain why a theory supported by a paper published in a scientific journal is not necessarily scientific 'fact'?
Q3 Explain why considering scientific evidence alone is not enough when making decisions in society.

Exam Question

Q1* A scientist has developed a proposal for a power station which generates electricity renewably from the energy of the tides, without producing greenhouse gases that can lead to climate change. The proposed location of the power station is off a stretch of scenic coastline that attracts a lot of tourism. She claims that her evidence suggests that if built in this location, the power station would produce sufficient electricity to entirely replace a nearby coal-fired power station that uses non-renewable fossil fuels and produces greenhouse gases. Discuss the economic, social and environmental factors that need to be considered by decision-makers considering her proposal. [6 marks]

* The quality of your extended response will be assessed in this question.

No. Borrowing your friend's homework to 'check' it is not peer review...

Hopefully these pages have given you a nice intro to the scientific process, e.g. what scientists do to provide you with 'facts'. You need to understand this, as you're expected to know how science works yourself — for the exam and for life.

Quantities and Units

Learning Physics is a lot like building a house — both involve drinking a lot of tea. Also, both have important foundations — if you skip this stuff everything else is likely to go a bit wrong. So, here goes brick-laying 101...

A **Physical Quantity** has both a **Numerical Value** and a **Unit**

1) Every time you measure or calculate a quantity you need to give the **units**.

2) There are seven **base quantities** from which all the other quantities you'll meet can be **derived**. These other quantities are called **derived quantities**.

3) The **Système International** (SI) includes a set of **base units** for the seven base quantities. The base quantities and their SI base units are:

Quantity	SI base unit
mass	kilogram, kg
length	metre, m
time	second, s
current	ampere, A
temperature	kelvin, K
amount of a substance	mole, mol
luminous intensity	candela, cd

Kilograms are a bit odd — they're the only SI unit with a scaling prefix (see the next page).

You're more likely to see temperatures given in °C.

4) The units for **derived quantities** can be derived from these base units. E.g. **force** is a derived quantity, with the SI derived unit of newtons, N. **1 N** is defined as equivalent to **1 kgms^{-2}**.

5) The derived quantities and SI derived units you'll need will be covered throughout the book and you need to remember them.

6) You also need to have a rough idea of the size of each SI base unit and SI derived unit in this book, so that you can **estimate quantities** using them.

Remembering how SI derived units are defined will help you make sure the other quantities in your equations are in the right units.

> **Example:** A man drops a ball from the first floor window of his house. It takes 1 s to hit the ground. Estimate the average speed of the ball.
>
> A first floor window of a normal house is about 6 m above the ground, so s = 6 m.
> speed = distance ÷ time = 6 m ÷ 1 s = 6 ms^{-1}

You Can **Work Out** Derived Units **Mathematically**

The units in any equation must always be the **same on both sides**.
You can use this rule to work out some of the simpler SI derived units, like speed:

> **Example:** Show that the SI derived unit for speed is ms^{-1} (speed = distance ÷ time).
>
> Distance is a length, so its SI base unit is the metre, m. The base unit of time is the second, s.
> To find the unit for speed, just put the units for distance and time into the equation for speed: **m ÷ s = ms^{-1}**

Some SI derived units have **special names**, like the newton. You can work out what they're **equivalent** to in **SI base units** using the same method as above.

> **Example:** Charge, Q, is measured in coulombs, C, and given by the equation charge = current × time. What is one coulomb equivalent to in SI base units?
>
> The SI base unit for current is the ampere, A, and the SI base unit for time is the second, s.
> Charge = current × time, so 1 C = 1 A × 1 s = **1 As**

Quantities and Units

Prefixes Let You Scale Units

Physical quantities come in a **huge range** of sizes. Prefixes are scaling factors that let you write numbers across this range without having to put everything in standard form.

These are the most common prefixes you'll come across:

prefix	femto (f)	pico (p)	nano (n)	micro (µ)	milli (m)	centi (c)	deci (d)	kilo (k)	mega (M)	giga (G)	tera (T)
multiple of unit	1×10^{-15}	1×10^{-12}	1×10^{-9}	1×10^{-6}	0.001 (1×10^{-3})	0.01 (1×10^{-2})	0.1 (1×10^{-1})	1000 (1×10^{3})	1×10^{6}	1×10^{9}	1×10^{12}

If you're a bit uncertain about moving directly between these scaling factors, then convert quantities into the standard unit before you do anything else with them:

> **Example 1:** Convert 1869 picometres into nanometres.
>
> First, convert the value to metres: 1869 pm = 1869×10^{-12} m
>
> Then divide by 1×10^{-9} to convert to nanometres: $1869 \times 10^{-12} \div 1 \times 10^{-9}$ = **1.869 nm**

Or, you can convert between prefixes directly:

> **Example 2:** Convert 0.247 megawatts into kilowatts.
>
> 1 MW = 1×10^{6} W and 1 kW = 1×10^{3} W
>
> So the scaling factor to move between MW and kW is: $(1 \times 10^{6}) \div (1 \times 10^{3}) = 1 \times 10^{3}$.
>
> So 0.247 MW = $0.247 \times 1 \times 10^{3}$ = **247 kW**

It's really easy to get muddled up when you're converting between prefixes. The rule is, if you're moving to the right in the table above, your number should get smaller, and if you're moving to the left the number should get larger. If your answer doesn't match the rule, you've made a mistake.

Don't use these prefixes in the middle of calculations — they'll change the units of your final answer, and could get you in a mess. You should generally convert to the units you need to use before you do any calculations, or once you've got a final answer.

Practice Questions

Q1 What is meant by a base quantity and a derived quantity?

Q2 What is the SI unit of mass?

Q3 What is meant by an SI base unit and an SI derived unit?

Q4 What is: a) 20 000 W in kilowatts
b) 2×10^{-6} W in milliwatts
c) 1.23×10^{7} W in gigawatts?

Aliona preferred scaling frozen waterfalls.

Exam Question

Q1 The density, ρ, of a material gives its mass per unit volume. It is given by $\rho = m/V$, where m = mass and V = volume.

a) Express the units of density in terms of SI base units. [1 mark]

b) Calculate the density of a cube of mass 9.8 g, and side length 11 mm. Give your answer in the units stated in part a). [2 marks]

c) A bath tub is filled with water. Given that the density of water is approximately 1000 kg m^{-3}, estimate the mass of the water in the bath tub. [2 marks]

What's the SI base unit for boring...

Not the most exciting pair of pages these, I'll admit, but it's important that you have the basics down, or else you're leaving yourself open to simple little mistakes that'll cost you marks. So make sure you've memorised all the SI base units in the table, then try and write down all the prefixes and their scaling factors. If you don't get them all first time, keep trying until you can. Remember, you need to know the units for every derived quantity you meet in this book, too.

Planning and Implementing

Science is all about getting good evidence to support (or disprove) your theories, so scientists need to be able to spot a badly designed experiment, interpret the results of an experiment or study, and design their own experiments too...

You Might have to **Design an Experiment** to Answer a **Question**

1) You might be asked to design a physics experiment to **investigate** something or answer a question.

2) It could be a **lab experiment** that you've seen before, a **new experiment** you aren't familiar with, or it could be something **applied**, like deciding which building material is best for a particular job.

3) Whatever you're asked, you'll be able to use the physics you know and the skills covered on the next few pages to figure out the best way to do the investigation.

A **Variable** is Anything that has the Potential to **Change** in an Experiment

1) First, you need to identify your **independent** and **dependent variables**:

> The **independent** variable is the thing you **change**.
> The **dependent** variable is the thing you **measure**.

Example 1: If you're investigating how changing the potential difference across a component affects the current through it, the **independent variable** is the **potential difference**, and the **dependent variable** is the **current**.

2) Apart from the independent and dependent variables, **all other variables** should stay the same during your experiment. If not, you can't tell whether or not the independent variable is responsible for any changes in your dependent variable, so your results won't be **valid** (p.12). This is known as **controlling variables**. It might be worth **measuring control variables** that are likely to change during your experiment to check that they really are under control.

Example 1 (continued): In the example above, you need to use the same **circuit components**, and to keep the **temperature** of the apparatus **constant** — e.g. by letting the circuit cool down between readings.

Example 2: If you're investigating the value of **acceleration due to gravity** by dropping an object and timing its fall, **draughts** in the room could really mess up your results. Picking an object that is more **resistant** to being blown about (like a ball-bearing) will help make your results more **precise** (p.12).

Select Appropriate **Apparatus** and **Techniques**

1) You need to think about what **units** your measurements of the independent and dependent variables are likely to be in before you begin (e.g. millimetres or metres, milliseconds or hours).

2) Think about the **range** you plan on taking measurements over too — e.g. if you're measuring the effect of increasing the force on a spring, you need to know whether you should increase the force in steps of 1 newton, 10 newtons or 100 newtons. Sometimes, you'll be able to **estimate** what effect changing your independent variable will have, or sometimes a **pilot experiment** might help.

3) Considering your measurements before you start will also help you choose the most appropriate **apparatus** and **techniques** for the experiment:

> There's a whole range of apparatus and techniques that could come up in your exam. Make sure you know how to use all the ones you've come across in class.

Example:

- If you're measuring the length of a **spring** that you're applying a force to, you might need a **ruler**. If you're measuring the diameter of a **wire**, you'd be better off with a set of **callipers**.

  If the wire **doesn't stretch** easily, you may need to use a **very long wire** to get an extension that's big enough to measure, so you might need to use a **pulley** like in the Young modulus experiment on p.60.

- If you're measuring a **time interval**, you could use a **stopwatch**. If the time is **really short** (for example if you're investigating acceleration due to gravity), you might need something more sensitive, like **light gates**.

4) Whatever apparatus and techniques you use, make sure you use them **correctly**. E.g. if you're measuring a length, make sure your eye is level with the ruler when you take the measurement.

5) While you're planning, you should also think about the **risks** involved in your experiment and how to manage them — e.g. if you're investigating a material that might snap, wear safety goggles to protect your eyes.

Planning and Implementing

Figure Out how to Record your Data Before you Start

Before you get going, you'll need a **data table** to record your results in.

1) It should include space for your **independent variable** and your **dependent variable**. You should specify the **units** in the headers, not within the table itself.

2) The readings of the **independent variable** should be taken at **evenly spaced intervals**.

3) Your table will need enough room for repeated measurements. You should aim to **repeat** each measurement at least **three times**. Taking repeat measurements can reduce the effect of random errors in your results (see p.12) and makes spotting **anomalous** results, like this one, much easier. If there's no way to take repeat readings, then you should **increase** the **total number** of readings that you take.

	Current / A			
P.d. / V	Trial 1	Trial 2	Trial 3	Average
1.00	0.052	0.047	0.050	0.050
1.50	0.079	0.075	0.077	0.077
2.00	0.303	0.098	0.097	...
2.50	0.129	0.125	0.130	...
3.00	0.149	0.151	0.145	...
...	...	...	...	...

4) There should be space in your table for any data processing you need to do, e.g. calculating an **average** from repeated measurements, or calculating speed from measurements of distance and time.

5) Most of the time, your data will be **quantitative** (i.e. you'll be recording numerical values). Occasionally, you may have to deal with **qualitative** data (data that can be observed but not measured with a numerical value). It's still best to record this kind of data in a table, to keep your results **organised**, but the layout may be a little **different**.

You Could be Asked to Evaluate An Experimental Design

If you need to evaluate an experimental design, whether it's your own or someone else's, you need to think about these sorts of things:

- Does the experiment **actually test** what it sets out to test?
- Is the method **clear** enough for someone else to follow?
- Apart from the **independent** and **dependent variables**, is everything else going to be **properly controlled**?
- Are the **apparatus** and **techniques appropriate** for what's being measured? Will they be used correctly?
- Are enough **repeated measurements** going to be taken?
- Is the experiment going to be conducted **safely**, for those involved and those **nearby**?
- Are there any other **ethical considerations**? For example, does the experiment produce **harmful waste products**? Is the apparatus being used in a way that won't **damage it**?

Greta was paying the price for not planning her experiment properly.

Practice Questions

Q1 What is meant by the term independent variable? What is a dependent variable?

Q2 Why do you need to plan to control all of the other variables in an experiment?

Q3 What do you need to consider when selecting your apparatus?

Q4 Why should you take repeated measurements in an experiment?

Exam Question

Q1 A student is investigating the effect of the light level on the resistance of an LDR (light-dependent resistor). The student connects the LDR to a power supply, and measures the resistance of the LDR at various distances from a light source using a multimeter.

a) State the independent and dependent variables for this experiment. [1 mark]

b) State two variables that the student needs to control in order to ensure his results are valid. [2 marks]

The best-planned experiments of mice and men...

...often get top marks. The details of planning and carrying out an experiment will vary a lot depending on what you're investigating, but if all this stuff is wedged in your brain you shouldn't go far wrong, so make sure you've got it learned.

Analysing Results

You've planned an experiment, and you've got some results (or you've been given some in your exam).
Now it's time to look into them a bit more closely...

Do any **Calculations** You Need to **First**

1) Before you calculate anything, check for any **anomalous results**. If there's something in the results that's **clearly wrong**, then don't include it in your calculations — it'll just **muck everything up**. Be careful though, you should only exclude an anomalous result if you have **good reason** to think it's wrong, e.g. it looks like a decimal point is in the **wrong place**, or you suspect that one of the control variables **changed**. And you should talk about any anomalous results when you're evaluating the experiment (pages 12-13).

2) For most experiments, you'll at least need to calculate the mean (average) of some **repeated measurements**:

$$\text{mean (average) of a measurement} = \frac{\text{sum of your repeated measurements}}{\text{number of repeats taken}}$$

In class, you could use a spreadsheet to process your data (and plot graphs), but it's important that you know how to do it by hand for the exam.

3) Calculate any quantities that you're interested in that you haven't **directly measured** (e.g. pressure, speed).

You should try to give any values you calculate to the **same number of significant figures** as the data value with the **fewest significant figures** in your calculation. If you give your result to too many significant figures, you're saying your final result is more **precise** than it actually is (see p.12).

Present Your Results on a **Graph**

Make sure you know how to plot a graph of your results:

If you need to use your graph to measure something, select axes that will let you do this easily (e.g. by measuring the gradient or the intercept, see the next page).

1) Usually, the **independent variable** goes on the *x*-axis and the **dependent variable** goes on the *y*-axis. Both axes should be **labelled** clearly, with the quantity and **units**. The **scales** used should be sensible (i.e. they should go up in sensible steps, and should spread the data out over the full graph rather than bunching it up in a corner).

2) Plot your points using a **sharp pencil**, to make sure they're as **accurate** as possible.

3) Draw a **line of best fit** for your results. Around **half** the data points should be above the line, and half should be below it (you should ignore anomalous results). Depending on the data, the line might be **straight**, or **curved**.

Graphs can Show Different Kinds of **Correlation**

Remember, correlation does not necessarily mean cause — p.3.

The **correlation** describes the relationship between the variables. Data can show:

Positive correlation:
As one variable increases the other increases.

Negative correlation:
As one variable increases the other decreases.

No correlation:
No relationship between the variables.

Analysing Results

You Might Need to Find a **Gradient** or **Intercept**

If the line of best fit is **straight**, then the graph is **linear**. This means a change in one always leads to a change in the other. The **line of best fit** for a linear graph has the **equation:** $y = mx + c$ Where **m** is the **gradient** of the line and **c** is the **y-intercept**.

If the line of best fit goes through the origin (c is 0), you can say the variables are **directly proportional** to each other: $y \propto x$ ∝ just means 'is directly proportional to'.

Example: This graph shows displacement against time for a motorbike travelling west. Find the bike's velocity.

For a displacement-time graph, the gradient gives the velocity (as velocity = displacement ÷ time).

$\Delta y = 1000 - 400 = 600$ m

$\Delta x = 56 - 16 = 40$ s

Δ means 'change in'.

The y intercept is 160. This means the bike's displacement was 160 m at time 0 s.

$$\text{velocity} = \frac{\text{displacement}}{\text{time}} = \frac{\Delta y}{\Delta x} = 600 \div 40 = \textbf{15 ms}^{-1}\textbf{ west}$$

If a graph has a **curved** line of best fit, you can find the gradient of a given point on the line by drawing a **tangent** to the curve (see page 23). It's sometimes helpful to choose axes that turn a curved graph into a straight one:

Example:

For a given force, the graph of **pressure** applied against the **area** that the force is applied over looks like this:

If you plot pressure against **1 ÷ area**, the graph looks like this:

pressure = force ÷ area.

The **gradient** is:
pressure ÷ (1 ÷ area)
= pressure × area
= force applied (p.64)

Practice Questions

Q1 Describe what you should do with anomalous results when processing data.

Q2 How do you calculate an average of repeated results?

Q3 Sketch a graph showing a negative correlation.

Exam Question

Q1 An engineer is investigating the performance of a prototype car with a new kind of environmentally-friendly engine. The data below shows the speed of the car, going from stationary to over 70 kilometres per hour. (In this question, you may use the formula: acceleration = change in speed ÷ time taken to change speed.)

Time / s	0.0	1.0	2.0	3.0	4.0	5.0	6.0	7.0
Speed / km per hour	0	3	8	22	40	54	66	70

a) Draw a graph showing speed against time for this data. [4 marks]

b) State the times, to the nearest second, between which the graph is linear. [1 mark]

c) Using the graph, calculate the maximum acceleration of the car. [4 marks]

My level of boredom is proportional to the time I've spent on this page...

This stuff can get a bit fiddly, especially measuring the gradient of a curved line, but for the most part it's not too bad, and you should have seen a lot of it before. So dust off your pencil sharpener, and get to work...

Measurements and Uncertainties

There are errors and uncertainties in every measurement. You need to be aware of them.

All Results have Some *Uncertainty*

The smallest measuring interval on an instrument gives you its resolution.

1) **Every** measurement you take has an **experimental uncertainty**.

2) The smallest uncertainty you can have in a measurement is the uncertainty due to the **resolution** of your equipment. It's ± **half** of one division on the measuring instrument used. E.g. using a thermometer with a scale where each division represents 2 °C, a measurement of 30 °C will at **best** be measured to be 30 ± 1 °C. And that's without taking into account any other errors that might be in your measurement.

3) The ± sign gives you the **range** in which the **true** length (the one you'd really like to know) probably lies. 30 ± 0.5 cm tells you the true length is very likely to lie in the range of 29.5 to 30.5 cm. The maximum difference between your value and the true value (here 0.5 cm) is sometimes called the **margin of error**.

4) There are two measures of uncertainty you need to know about:

> **Absolute uncertainty** — the **total uncertainty** for a measurement.
>
> **Percentage uncertainty** — the uncertainty given as a **percentage** of the measurement.
> Measuring **larger** values reduces the percentage uncertainty.

5) An uncertainty should also include a level of **confidence** or probability, to indicate how **likely** the true value is to lie in the interval. The **more variation** there is in your results, and the **fewer repeats** you have done, the **less confident** you can be.

6) The uncertainty on a **mean** (see p.8) of repeated results is the **largest difference** between the mean and any of the values used to calculate it. So if you take repeated measurements of a current and get values of 0.1 A, 0.4 A and 0.4 A, the mean current is 0.3 A, and the uncertainty on the mean is 0.3 − 0.1 = ± **0.2 A**. You can estimate the uncertainty on the mean as **half the range** — e.g. (0.4 − 0.1) ÷ 2 = **0.15 A**.

7) If no uncertainty is given for a value, the **assumed uncertainty** is **half the increment** of the **last** significant figure that the value is **given** to. E.g. 2.0 is given to 2 **significant figures**, so you would assume an uncertainty of 0.05. You should always assume the **largest** amount of uncertainty when doing an experiment.

Sometimes You Need to *Combine Uncertainties*

You have to combine the uncertainties of different measured values to find the uncertainty of a calculated result:

Adding *or* Subtracting *Data* — ADD *the* Absolute Uncertainties

Example: A wire is stretched from 4.3 ± 0.1 cm to 5.5 ± 0.1 cm. Calculate the extension of the wire.

1) First subtract the lengths without the uncertainty values: 5.5 − 4.3 = 1.2 cm
2) Then find the total uncertainty by adding the individual absolute uncertainties: 0.1 + 0.1 = 0.2 cm
So, the extension of the wire is **1.2 ± 0.2 cm**.

Multiplying *or* Dividing *Data* — ADD *the* Percentage Uncertainties

Example: A force of 15 N ± 3% is applied to a stationary object which has a mass of 6.0 ± 0.3 kg. Calculate the acceleration of the object and state the percentage uncertainty in this value.

1) First calculate the acceleration without uncertainty: $a = F \div m = 15 \div 6.0 = 2.5 \ \text{ms}^{-2}$
2) Next, calculate the percentage uncertainty in the mass: % uncertainty in $m = \frac{0.3}{6.0} \times 100 = 5\%$
3) Add the percentage uncertainties in the force and mass values to find the total uncertainty in the acceleration: Total uncertainty = 3% + 5% = 8%
So, the acceleration = **2.5 ms^{-2} ± 8%**

Raising *to a* Power — MULTIPLY *the* Percentage Uncertainty *by the* Power

Example: The radius of a circle is $r = 40$ cm ± 2.5%. Find the percentage uncertainty in the circle's area (πr^2).

The radius is raised to the power of **2** to calculate the area. So, the percentage uncertainty is 2.5% × 2 = **5%**

Measurements and Uncertainties

Error Bars Show the Uncertainty of Individual Points

1) Most of the time, you work out the **uncertainty** in your **final** result using the uncertainty in **each measurement** you make.

2) When you're plotting a **graph**, you can show the uncertainty in **each measurement** by using **error bars** to show the **range** the point is likely to lie in.

3) You can have error bars for just one variable (see below), or **both** the dependent and the independent variable. Error bars on both variables give you an '**error box**' for each point.

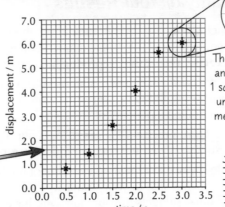

This is an 'error box'. The true value of the data point could lie anywhere in this area.

The error bars extend 1 square right and left for each measurement, and 1 square up and down. This gives an uncertainty of ± 0.1 s in each time measurement, and ± 0.2 m in each displacement measurement.

Your line of best fit (p.8) should always go through all of the error bars (see below) or boxes.

You Can Calculate the Uncertainty of Final Results from a Line of Best Fit

Normally when you draw a graph you'll want to find the **gradient** or **intercept** (p.9). For example, you can calculate k, the **force constant** of the object being stretched, from the **gradient** of the graph on the right — here it's about 20 000 Nm⁻¹. You can find the **uncertainty** in that value by using **worst lines**:

1) Draw lines of best fit which have the **maximum** and **minimum** possible slopes for the data and which should go through all of the **error bars** (see the pink and blue lines on the right). These are the **worst lines** for your data. If your data has errors in **both** the independent and dependent variables, then the worst lines should go through the **corners** of the error boxes.

2) Calculate the **gradients** of the worst lines. The blue line's gradient is about 21 000 Nm⁻¹ and the pink line's gradient is about 19 000 Nm⁻¹.

3) The **uncertainty** in the gradient is given by half the **difference** between the **worst gradients** — here it's 1000 Nm⁻¹. So this is the uncertainty in the value of the force constant. For this object, the force constant is 20 000 ± 1000 Nm⁻¹ (or 20 000 Nm⁻¹ ± 5%).

When the force is 0 N the extension is 0 mm — this is a measurement with no uncertainty.

4) Similarly, the uncertainty in the y-intercept is just half the **difference** between the **worst** intercepts (although there's no uncertainty here since the worst lines both go through the origin).

Practice Questions

Q1 What is meant by experimental uncertainty? How does it relate to an instrument's resolution?

Q2 What are the rules for combining uncertainties?

Q3 What are worst lines? How could you use them to find the uncertainty in the intercept of a graph?

Exam Question

Q1 A student is investigating the acceleration of a remote controlled car. The car has an initial velocity of 0.52 ± 0.02 ms⁻¹ and accelerates to 0.94 ± 0.02 ms⁻¹ over an interval of 2.5 ± 0.5 s.

   a) Calculate the percentage uncertainty in the car's initial speed. [1 mark]

   b) Calculate the percentage uncertainty in the car's final speed. [1 mark]

   c) Calculate the car's average acceleration over this interval. Include the absolute uncertainty of the result in your answer. (acceleration = change in velocity ÷ time taken). [4 marks]

My percentage uncertainty about these pages is 0.99%...

Uncertainties are a bit of a pain, but they're really important. Learn the rules for combining uncertainties, and make sure you know how to draw those pesky error bars, and what to do with them when you've got them.

Evaluating and Concluding

Once you've drawn your graphs and analysed your results, you need to think about your conclusions.

Evaluate the Quality of Your Results

Before you draw any conclusions, you should think about the quality of the results —
if the quality's not great you won't be able to have much confidence in your conclusion.
Good results are **valid**, **precise**, **repeatable**, **reproducible** and **accurate**.

Quality control — also important in construction.

1) **Valid measurements** measure what they're supposed to be measuring. If you haven't
   controlled all the variables (p.6) then your **results** won't be valid, because you won't
   just be testing the effect of the independent variable.

2) You can say your results are **precise** if the **range** that your repeated data is spread over is small.
   The precision of a result is only influenced by **random errors** (see below).

3) Results are **repeatable** if **you** can **repeat** an experiment multiple times and get the **same results**.
   You can measure the repeatability of your results by looking at their **precision**, and by comparing
   them to the results of other students in your class who have used exactly the same method and equipment.

4) For a result to be **reproducible**, it needs to be obtained by **different experimenters**, using **different equipment** and
   different methods. Testing whether a result is reproducible is a better test of its quality than testing whether it is
   repeatable, as it's less likely that the same **systematic errors** could have affected both methods (see below).

5) An **accurate result** is one that's really close to the **true value**. You often **can't know** the accuracy of a result, since
   you can never know the true value of what you're measuring. The exception to this is if you're measuring a **known
   constant**, like *g*, which has been **tested many times**, and is known to a good degree of certainty. In cases like this,
   you can assess how accurate your results are by **comparing** them to this known value. One way of
   doing this is by calculating the **percentage difference** — the difference between your result and the true value,
   expressed as a **percentage** of the **true value**.

You'll Need to Think About Random and Systematic Errors

An error is the difference between your **measured value** and the **true value** of whatever you're trying to measure.
There are two different kinds of error that could affect the quality of your results — **random errors** and **systematic
errors**. You should think about these when you're planning your experiment (so you can minimise them) and when
you're evaluating your results.

Systematic Errors

1) **Systematic errors** (including **zero errors**) are the same every time you repeat the experiment (they
   shift all the values by the same amount). They may be caused by the **equipment** you're using or
   how it's **set-up**, e.g. not lining up a ruler correctly when measuring the extension of a spring.

2) Systematic errors are really **hard to spot**, and they affect the **accuracy** of your results, but not the **precision**
   — so it can look like you've measured something **really well**, even if your results are actually **completely
   off**. Systematic errors might show up when you **compare results** with other people in your class who have
   done the **same experiment** if they're caused by a mistake you made, or when you compare your results
   with someone else who used a **different method** if there is something wrong with the procedure itself
   (i.e. when you check the reproducibility of your results).

3) It's always worth **checking your apparatus** at the start of an experiment, e.g. measure a few known
   masses to check that a mass balance is **calibrated** properly to make systematic errors less likely.

Random Errors

1) **Random errors** vary — they're what make the results a bit different each time you repeat an experiment.
   For example, if you measured the length of a wire 20 times, the chances are you'd get a slightly different
   value each time, e.g. due to your head being in a slightly different position when reading the scale. It could
   be that you just can't keep controlled variables (p.6) exactly the same throughout the experiment.

2) Unlike systematic errors, you can at least generally tell when random
   errors are there, as they affect your precision.

3) Using apparatus with a **better resolution** (p.10) can reduce the
   size of random errors in **individual measurements**.

4) Doing more **repeats** can also reduce the effect of random errors on **calculated results** like the mean (p.8).

Evaluating and Concluding

Draw **Conclusions** that Your Results **Support**

Your conclusion can't be more precise than the margin given by the uncertainty in your results.

1) A conclusion **explains** what the data shows.
   You can only draw a valid conclusion if you have valid data **supporting** it.

2) Your conclusion should be limited to the **circumstances you've tested** it under —
   if you've been investigating how the current flowing through a resistor changes with the
   potential difference across it, and have only used potential differences between 0 and 6 V, you can't claim to
   know what would happen if you used a potential difference of 100 V, or if you used a different resistor.

3) You also need to think about how much you can **believe** your conclusion, by evaluating the quality of
   your results (see previous page). If you can't believe your results, you can't form a **strong conclusion**.

Think About how the Experiment Could be **Improved**

Having collected the data, is there anything you think should have been done **differently**?
Were there any **limitations** to your method?

1) If the results aren't **valid**, could you change the experiment to fix this, e.g. by changing the data you're collecting?

2) If the results aren't **accurate**, what could have caused this?
   If there are **systematic errors** in your results, what could you do to prevent them?

3) Are there any changes you could make to the **apparatus** or **procedure** that would make the results more **precise**?

   - There are some simple ways to reduce **random errors** or their effects (see p.12), including
     using the most **appropriate** equipment, (e.g. swapping a millimetre ruler for a micrometer to
     measure the diameter of a wire) and **increasing** the number of **repeats**.
   - You can also use a **computer** to collect data — e.g. using light gates to measure a time
     interval rather than a **stopwatch**. This makes results more **precise** by reducing **human error**.

4) Are there any other ways you could have **reduced the errors** in the measurements?

Practice Questions

Q1 What is a valid result?
Q2 What is the difference between a repeatable result and a reproducible result?
Q3 What is the difference between saying the results of an experiment are precise and saying that they are accurate?
Q4 Give two examples of possible sources of random error and one example of a possible source of systematic
   error in an experiment. Which kind of error won't affect the precision of the results?
Q5 What should you think about when you are trying to improve an experimental design?

Exam Question

Q1 A student is investigating how the speed of a falling object is affected by
   how long it has been falling for. He drops an object from heights between
   10 cm and 60 cm and measures its speed at the end of its fall, and the time
   the fall takes, using light gates. He plots a graph of the final speed of the
   object against the time it took to fall, as shown on the left.

   a) Identify the anomalous result. [1 mark]

   b) The student concludes that the speed of any falling object is
      always proportional to the time it has been falling for.
      Explain whether or not the results support this conclusion. [2 marks]

In conclusion, Physics causes headaches...

*Valid, precise, repeatable, reproducible and accurate... you'd think they all mean the same thing, but they really don't.
Make sure you know the difference, and are careful about which one you use, or you'll be throwing marks away.*

Scalars and Vectors

And now time to draw some lovely triangles. Please, don't all thank me at once...

Scalars Only Have Size, but Vectors Have Size and Direction

1) A **scalar** has **no direction** — it's **just an amount** of something, like the **mass** of a **sack of meaty dog food**.

2) A **vector** has magnitude (**size**) and **direction** — like the **speed and direction** of next door's **cat** running away.

3) **Force, velocity and momentum** are all **vectors** — you need to know **which way** they're going as well as **how big** they are. Here are some of the common scalars and vectors that you'll come across in your exams:

Scalars	Vectors
mass, time, energy temperature, length, speed	displacement, force, velocity, acceleration, momentum

4) Vectors are drawn as **arrows** (to show their direction) with their **size** written next to them (see Example 1 below). In the exam, you might see quantities written with **arrows** above them, e.g. $\vec{v}$, to show that they're vectors.

*Sometimes vectors are printed in bold, e.g. **v**, but it's quite hard to handwrite in bold, so the arrow is used too.*

You can Add Vectors to Find the Resultant

1) Adding two or more vectors is called finding the **resultant** of them.

2) You should always start by drawing a **diagram**. Draw the vectors '**tip to tail**'. If you're doing a **vector subtraction**, draw the vector you're subtracting with the same magnitude but pointing in the **opposite direction**.

3) If the vectors are at **right angles** to each other, then you can use **Pythagoras** and **trigonometry** to find the resultant.

4) If the vectors aren't at right angles, you may need to draw a **scale diagram**.

Example 1: Jemima goes for a walk. She walks 3.0 m north and 4.0 m east. She has walked 7.0 m but she isn't 7.0 m from her starting point. Find the magnitude and direction of her displacement.

First, draw the vectors **tip-to-tail**. Then draw a line from the **tail** of the first vector to the **tip** of the last vector to give the **resultant**:

Because the vectors are at right angles, you get the **magnitude** of the resultant using Pythagoras:

$R^2 = 3.0^2 + 4.0^2 = 25.0$　　So　　$R = \mathbf{5.0\ m}$

Jemima's 'displacement' gives her position relative to her starting point, see p.16.

Now find the **bearing** of Jemima's new position from her original position.

You use the triangle again, but this time you need to use trigonometry. You know the opposite and the adjacent sides, so you can use:

$\tan \theta = 4.0 / 3.0$　　So　　$\theta = \mathbf{053°}$ **(to 2 s.f.)**

Jemima

Example 2: A van is accelerating north, with a resultant force of 510 N. A wind begins to blow on a bearing of 150°. It exerts a force of 200 N (to 2 s.f.) on the van. What is the new resultant force acting on the van?

A bearing is just an angle measured clockwise from the north line, represented by three digits, e.g. 10° = 010°.

The vectors **aren't** at right angles, so you need to do a scale drawing. Pick a sensible scale. Here, 1 cm = 100 N seems good.

Using a really sharp pencil, draw the initial resultant force on the van. As the van is going north, this should be a 5.1 cm long line going straight up.

The force of the wind acts on a bearing of 150°, so add this to your diagram. Using the same scale, this vector has a length of 2.0 cm.

Then you can draw on the new resultant force and measure its length. Measure the angle carefully to get the bearing.

The resultant force has a magnitude of 350 N (to 2 s.f.), acting on a bearing of 017° (to 2 s.f.).

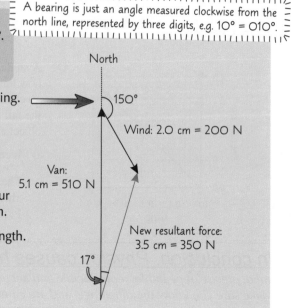

Scalars and Vectors

It's Useful to Split a Vector into Horizontal and Vertical Components

This is the opposite of finding the resultant — it's called **resolving**. You start from the resultant vector and split it into two **components** at right angles to each other. You're basically **working backwards** from Example 1 on the last page.

Resolving a vector v into horizontal and vertical components:

You get the **horizontal** component v_h like this:

$$\cos \theta = v_h / v$$

$$\boxed{v_h = v \cos \theta}$$

...and the **vertical** component v_v like this:

$$\sin \theta = v_v / v$$

$$\boxed{v_v = v \sin \theta}$$

Where θ is the angle from the horizontal.

Example: Charley's amazing floating home is travelling at a speed of 5.0 ms^{-1} at an angle of 60° (to 2 s.f.) up from the horizontal. Find the vertical and horizontal components.

The **horizontal** component v_h is:

$$v_h = v \cos \theta = 5.0 \cos 60° = \textbf{2.5 } \textbf{ms}^{-1}$$

The **vertical** component v_v is:

$$v_v = v \sin \theta = 5.0 \sin 60° = \textbf{4.3 } \textbf{ms}^{-1} \textbf{ (to 2 s.f.)}$$

Charley's mobile home was the envy of all his friends.

You can also resolve vectors using **scale drawings**. It's easiest to do this on **squared paper**. Just draw the vector to **scale** in the **correct direction**, then draw a **horizontal** line and **vertical** line from the tip and tail of the vector to form a **right-angled triangle**. Then measure the **lengths** of the lines and use the **scale** to convert them — this gives you the **horizontal** and **vertical** components of the vector.

Resolving is dead useful because the two components of a vector **don't affect each other**. This means you can deal with the two directions **completely separately** (there's more on this on page 20).

Practice Questions

Q1 What is the difference between a vector and a scalar? Give three vector quantities and three scalar quantities.

Q2 Describe how to draw a vector, and how to use vector notation.

Q3 Describe how to use a scale diagram to: a) find a resultant vector
  b) resolve a vector into components at right angles to each other.

Exam Questions

Q1 The wind applies a horizontal force of 20.0 N on a falling rock of weight 75 N.
Calculate the magnitude and direction of the resultant force. [2 marks]

Q2 A glider is travelling at a velocity of 20.0 ms^{-1} at an angle of 15.0° below the horizontal.
Calculate the horizontal and vertical components of the glider's velocity. [2 marks]

Q3 A remote controlled boat is placed in a river. The boat produces a driving speed of 1.54 ms^{-1} at an angle of 60.0° to the current (travelling with the current). The river is flowing at 0.20 ms^{-1}.
By resolving the vectors into their horizontal and vertical components, show that the resultant velocity of the boat is 1.6 ms^{-1} at an angle of 54° to the current. [4 marks]

I think I'm a scalar quantity, my Mum says I'm completely direction-less...

Lots of different ways to solve vector problems on these pages, it must be your lucky day. Trigonometry comes up all over the shop in physics, so make sure you're completely okay with it. Remember: **S**in θ = **O**pposite ÷ **H**ypotenuse, **C**os θ = **A**djacent ÷ **H**ypotenuse, and **T**an θ = **O**pposite ÷ **A**djacent. Or SOH CAH TOA.

Motion with Uniform Acceleration

All the equations on this page are for motion with constant acceleration. It makes life a whole lot easier, trust me.

Learn the **Definitions** of **Speed**, **Displacement**, **Velocity** and **Acceleration**

Displacement, velocity and acceleration are all **vector** quantities (page 14), so the **direction** matters.

> **Speed** — How fast something is moving, regardless of direction.
> **Displacement** (s) — How far an object's travelled from its starting point in a given direction.
> **Velocity** (v) — The rate of change of an object's displacement (its speed in a given direction).
> **Acceleration** (a) — The rate of change of an object's velocity.

During a journey, the **average speed** is just the **total distance** covered over the **total time** elapsed.
The speed of an object at any given point in time is known as its **instantaneous** speed.

Uniform Acceleration is Constant Acceleration

Acceleration could mean a change in speed or direction or both.

Uniform means constant here. It's nothing to do with what you wear.
There are **four main equations** that you use to solve problems involving **uniform acceleration**. You need to be able to **use them**, but you don't have to know how they're **derived** — we've just put it in to help you learn them.

1) **Acceleration is the rate of change of velocity.**
From this definition you get:

$$a = \frac{(v - u)}{t} \quad \text{so} \quad \boxed{v = u + at}$$

where:
u = initial velocity a = acceleration
v = final velocity t = time taken

2) s = **average velocity × time**
If acceleration is constant, the average velocity is just the average of the initial and final velocities, so:

$$\boxed{s = \frac{(u + v)t}{2}} \quad s = \text{displacement}$$

3) Substitute the expression for v from equation **1** into equation **2** to give:

$$s = \frac{(u + u + at) \times t}{2}$$
$$= \frac{2ut + at^2}{2}$$

$$\boxed{s = ut + \tfrac{1}{2}at^2}$$

4) You can **derive** the fourth equation from equations **1** and **2**:

Use equation **1** in the form: $a = \dfrac{v - u}{t}$ Multiply both sides by s, where: $s = \dfrac{(u + v)}{2} \times t$

This gives us: $as = \dfrac{(v - u)}{t} \times \dfrac{(u + v)t}{2}$

The t's on the right cancel, so:
$2as = (v - u)(v + u)$
$2as = v^2 - uv + uv - u^2$

so: $\boxed{v^2 = u^2 + 2as}$

Example: A tile falls from a roof 25.0 m high. Calculate its speed when it hits the ground and how long it takes to fall. Take g = 9.81 ms⁻².

First of all, write out what you know:
$s = 25.0$ m
$u = 0$ ms⁻¹ since the tile's stationary to start with
$a = 9.81$ ms⁻² due to gravity
$v = ?$ $t = ?$

> Usually you take upwards as the positive direction. In this question it's probably easier to take downwards as positive, so you get $g = +9.81$ ms⁻² instead of $g = -9.81$ ms⁻².

9.81 ms⁻²

25.0 m

Then, choose an equation with only **one unknown quantity**.
So start with $v^2 = u^2 + 2as$
$v^2 = 0 + 2 \times 9.81 \times 25.0$
$v^2 = 490.5$ $v = \textbf{22.1 ms}^{-1}$ **(to 3 s.f.)**

Now, find t using:
$s = ut + \tfrac{1}{2}at^2$
$25.0 = 0 + \tfrac{1}{2} \times 9.81 \times t^2$
$t^2 = \dfrac{25.0}{4.905}$

Final answers:
$t = \textbf{2.26 s}$ **(to 3 s.f.)**
$v = \textbf{22.1 ms}^{-1}$ **(to 3 s.f.)**

Motion with Uniform Acceleration

Example: A car accelerates steadily from rest at a rate of 4.2 ms⁻² for 6.5 seconds.

4.2 ms⁻²

a) Calculate the final speed.

b) Calculate the distance travelled in 6.5 seconds.

Remember — always start by writing down what you know.

a) $a = 4.2$ ms⁻²   choose the right equation... $v = u + at$

$u = 0$ ms⁻¹ $v = 0 + 4.2 \times 6.5$

$t = 6.5$ s   **Final answer:** $v = 27.3$ ms⁻¹

$v = ?$ $= \mathbf{27}$ **ms⁻¹ (to 2 s.f.)**

b) $s = ?$ **you can use:** $s = \dfrac{(u + v)t}{2}$ **or:** $s = ut + \frac{1}{2}at^2$

$t = 6.5$ s

$u = 0$ ms⁻¹

$a = 4.2$ ms⁻² $s = \dfrac{(0 + 27.3) \times 6.5}{2}$ $s = 0 + \frac{1}{2} \times 4.2 \times (6.5)^2$

$v = 27.3$ ms⁻¹

Final answer: $s = \mathbf{89}$ **m (to 2 s.f.)** $s = \mathbf{89}$ **m (to 2 s.f.)**

Practice Questions

Q1 Write down definitions for speed, displacement, average velocity, instantaneous velocity and acceleration.

Q2 Write out the four constant acceleration equations.

Mona's experiments into uniform acceleration had gone a bit far.

Exam Questions

Q1 A skydiver jumps from an aeroplane when it is flying horizontally. She accelerates due to gravity for 5.0 s.

a) Calculate her maximum vertical velocity. (Assume no air resistance.) [2 marks]

b) Calculate how far she falls in this time. [2 marks]

Q2 A motorcyclist slows down uniformly as he approaches a red light.
He takes 3.2 seconds to come to a halt and travels 40 m (to 2 s.f.) in this time.

a) Calculate how fast he was travelling initially. [2 marks]

b) Calculate his acceleration. (N.B. a negative value shows a deceleration.) [2 marks]

Q3 A stream provides a constant acceleration of 6 ms⁻². A toy boat is pushed directly against the current and then released from a point 1.2 m upstream from a small waterfall. Just before it reaches the waterfall, it is travelling at a speed of 5 ms⁻¹.

a) Calculate the initial velocity of the boat. [2 marks]

b) Calculate the maximum distance upstream from the waterfall the boat reaches. [2 marks]

Constant acceleration — it'll end in tears...

If a question talks about "uniform" or "constant" acceleration, it's a dead giveaway they want you to use one of these equations. The tricky bit is working out which one to use — start every question by writing out what you know and what you need to know. That makes it much easier to see which equation you need. To be sure. Arrr.

Free Fall

Free fall is all about objects falling — no really, that's all that the next two pages are about. Have fun.

Free Fall is when there's Only Gravity and Nothing Else

1) All objects on Earth experience a **force** due to the Earth's **gravitational field** that depends on their **mass**.

2) The **gravitational field strength** near the surface of the Earth is called **g** and is equal to **9.81 Nkg⁻¹**. **g** is given by the equation: $g = \frac{F}{m}$
   Where *m* is the mass of the object and *F* is the force due to gravity.

3) The force on an object due to gravity is called its **weight** (see page 38).

4) When the only force acting on an object is its weight, it will undergo **free fall**, and will **accelerate towards the ground**.

Force and acceleration are both vector quantities (p.14). In free fall, they act vertically downwards.

5) Acceleration and force are related by **F = ma**.
   So, for an object in free fall, $a = \frac{F}{m} = g$.

> Objects undergoing free fall on Earth have an acceleration of **g = 9.81 ms⁻²**.

It seems weird that *g* is both a gravitational field strength, in Nkg⁻¹, and an acceleration, in ms⁻². However, if you break down Nkg⁻¹ into SI units, they are actually the same as ms⁻².

6) Objects can have an initial velocity in any direction and still undergo **free fall** as long as the **force** providing the initial velocity is **no longer acting**.

You can Replace a with g in the Equations of Motion

You need to be able to work out **speeds**, **distances** and **times** for objects in **free fall**. Since *g* is a **constant acceleration** you can use the **constant acceleration equations**. *g* acts **downwards**, so you need to be careful about directions. To make it clear, there's a sign convention: **upwards is positive, downwards is negative**.

$$v = u + gt \qquad s = ut + \tfrac{1}{2}gt^2$$
$$v^2 = u^2 + 2gs \qquad s = \frac{(u + v)t}{2}$$

> *g* is always **downwards** so it's **usually negative** *t* is **always positive**
> *u* and *v* can be **positive or negative** *s* can be **positive or negative**

If an object is dropped, not thrown, *u* is zero.

You Can Calculate g By Performing an Experiment...

See pages 6-13 for more on doing experiments.

This is just one way of **measuring g**, there are loads of different experiments you could do — just make sure you know **one** method for your exams.

1) Set up the equipment shown in the diagram on the right.

2) Measure the height *h* from the **bottom** of the ball bearing to the **trapdoor**.

3) Flick the switch to simultaneously **start the timer** and **disconnect the electromagnet**, releasing the ball bearing.

4) The ball bearing falls, knocking the trapdoor down and **breaking the circuit** — which **stops the timer**. Record the time *t* shown on the timer.

5) **Repeat** this experiment three times and **average** the time taken to fall from this height. Repeat this experiment but drop the ball from several **different heights**.

6) You can then use these results to find *g* using a **graph** (see the next page).

- Using a small and heavy ball bearing means you can assume air resistance is so small you can **ignore it**.

- Having a computer **automatically release** and **time** the ball-bearing's fall can measure times with a **smaller uncertainty** than if you tried to drop the ball and time the fall using a stopwatch.

- The most significant source of **error** in this experiment will be in the measurement of *h*. Using a ruler, you'll have an uncertainty of about ±1 mm. This dwarfs any error from switch delay or air resistance. By making the values of *h* as **large** as possible, you can reduce the **percentage uncertainty** in your measurement of the height, (see p.10) as well as the percentage uncertainty caused by the **resolution** of the timer (as the bigger *h* is, the longer the ball-bearing will take to fall).

Free Fall

...and Plotting a **Graph** of Your **Results**

1) Use your data from the experiment on the last page to plot a graph of **height** (s) against the **time** it takes the ball to fall, **squared** (t^2). Then draw a **line of best fit**.

Height / m (y-axis), Time taken to fall squared / 10^{-2} s² (x-axis)

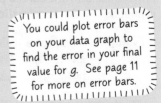

You could plot error bars on your data graph to find the error in your final value for g. See page 11 for more on error bars.

2) You know that with constant acceleration, $s = ut + \frac{1}{2}at^2$. If you drop the ball, initial speed $u = 0$, so $s = \frac{1}{2}at^2$.

3) Rearranging this gives $\frac{1}{2}a = \frac{s}{t^2}$, or $\frac{1}{2}g = \frac{s}{t^2}$ (remember the acceleration is all due to gravity).

In the exam you might be asked to find g from a displacement-time graph (see p.22-23). g is an acceleration and the gradient of the graph will be velocity, so you can find g by finding the change in gradient between two points on the graph (as $a = \Delta v \div \Delta t$).

4) So the gradient of the line of best fit, $\frac{\Delta s}{\Delta t^2}$, is equal to $\frac{1}{2}g$:

$$g = 2 \times \frac{\Delta s}{\Delta t^2} = 2 \times \frac{0.43}{0.090} = 9.555...$$
$$= 9.6 \text{ ms}^{-2} \text{ (to 2 s.f.)}$$

5) As you know g (9.8 ms⁻² to 2 s.f.) you can calculate the **percentage difference** (see p.12) between your value of g and the true value, and use this to evaluate the **accuracy** of your results.

$$\% \text{ difference} = \frac{9.6 - 9.8}{9.8} \times 100\% = -2.040...$$
$$= -2.0\% \text{ (to 2 s.f.)}$$

Practice Questions

Q1 State the equation linking gravitational field strength, force due to gravity, and mass.

Q2 What is the value of the acceleration of a free-falling object on Earth?

Q3 Describe how you would find a value for g by using a trapdoor and electromagnet set-up.

Exam Questions

Q1 A student has designed a device to estimate the value of 'g'. It consists of two narrow strips of card joined by a piece of transparent plastic. The student measures the widths of the strips of card then drops the device through a light gate connected to a computer. As the device falls, the strips of card break the light beam.

    a) Give three pieces of data that the student will need from the computer to estimate g.   [3 marks]

    b) Explain how these measurements can be used to estimate 'g'.   [3 marks]

    c) Give one reason why the student's value of 'g' will not be entirely accurate.   [1 mark]

Q2 Jan bounces on a trampoline, reaching a point 5.0 m above the trampoline's surface. Assume there is no air resistance.

    a) Calculate the speed with which she leaves the trampoline surface.   [2 marks]

    b) Calculate how long it takes Jan to reach her highest point.   [2 marks]

    c) State her velocity as she lands back on the trampoline.   [1 mark]

It's not the falling that hurts — it's the being pelted with rotten vegetables... okay, okay...

The hardest bit with free fall questions is getting your signs right. Draw yourself a little diagram before you start doing any calculations, and label it with what you know and what you want to know.

Projectile Motion

Any object given an initial velocity then left to move freely under gravity is a projectile. Time to resolve some vectors...

You have to think of **Horizontal** and **Vertical** Motion **Separately**

In projectiles, the **horizontal** and **vertical** components of the object's motion are **completely independent**. Projectiles follow a **curved path** because the horizontal velocity remains **constant**, while the vertical velocity is affected by the **acceleration due to gravity**, g.

Example: Jane fires a scale model of a TV talent show presenter horizontally from 1.5 m above the ground with a velocity of 100 ms⁻¹ (to 2 s.f.). How long does it take to hit the ground, and how far does it travel horizontally? Assume the model acts as a particle, the ground is horizontal and there's no air resistance.

Think about vertical motion first:

1) It's **constant acceleration** under gravity...

2) You know $u = 0$ (no vertical velocity at first), $s = -1.5$ m and $a = g = -9.81$ ms⁻². You need to find t.

3) Use $s = \frac{1}{2}gt^2 \Rightarrow t = \sqrt{\frac{2s}{g}} = \sqrt{\frac{2 \times -1.5}{-9.81}} = 0.553...$ s. So the model hits the ground after **0.55 (to 2 s.f.)** seconds.

Then do the horizontal motion:

1) The horizontal motion isn't affected by gravity or any other force, so it moves at a **constant speed**. That means you can just use good old **speed = distance / time**.

2) Now $v_h = 100$ ms⁻¹, $t = 0.553...$ s and $a = 0$. You need to find s_h.

3) $s_h = v_h t = 100 \times 0.553... = $ **55 m (to 2 s.f.)**

Where v_h is the horizontal velocity, and s_h is the horizontal distance travelled (rather than the height fallen).

It's **Slightly Trickier** if it **Starts Off** at an **Angle**

If something's projected at an **angle** (e.g. a javelin) you'll start with **horizontal** and **vertical velocity**. Here's what to do:

1) **Resolve** the initial velocity into **horizontal** and **vertical** components:

2) Often you'll use the vertical component to work out **how long** it's in the air and/or **how high** it goes, and the horizontal component to work out **how far** it goes while it's in the air.

If an object has velocity v, at an angle of θ to the horizontal:

The horizontal component of its velocity is: $\boxed{v_h = v \cos \theta}$

The vertical component of its velocity is: $\boxed{v_v = v \sin \theta}$

(see page 15)

Example: An athlete throws a javelin from a height of 1.8 m with a velocity of 21 ms⁻¹ at an upward angle of 45° to the ground. How far is the javelin thrown? Assume the javelin acts as a particle, the ground is horizontal and there is no air resistance.

1) Draw a quick sketch of the information given in the question.

2) Start by resolving the velocity into horizontal and vertical components:
$u_h = \cos 45° \times 21 = 14.84...$ ms⁻¹
$u_v = \sin 45° \times 21 = 14.84...$ ms⁻¹

3) Then find how long it's in the air for — start by finding v_v. The javelin starts from a height of 1.8 m and finishes at ground level, so its final vertical distance $s_v = -1.8$ m:
$v_v^2 = u_v^2 + 2gs$
$v_v = \sqrt{14.84...^2 + 2 \times (-9.81) \times (-1.8)} = -15.99...$ ms⁻¹

You need the negative square root, as this is a velocity towards the ground.

Now you can use this v_v value and $s = \frac{(u+v)t}{2}$ to find the time it stays in the air:

$s_v = \frac{(u_v + v_v)t}{2} \Rightarrow t = \frac{s_v}{(u_v + v_v)} \times 2 = \frac{-1.8}{14.84... - 15.99...} \times 2 = 3.144...$ s

4) Finally, as $a_h = 0$, you can use **speed = distance / time** to work out how far it travels horizontally in this time. The horizontal velocity is just u_h, so: $s_h = u_h t = 14.84... \times 3.144... = 46.68... = $ **47 m (to 2 s.f.)**

Projectile Motion

You can Investigate Projectile Motion Using a **Video Camera...**

If you **video** a projectile moving, you can use **video analysis software** to investigate its motion:

1) You can **plot the course** taken by an object by recording its **position** in **each frame**.

2) If you know the **frame rate**, and your video includes a metre ruler or grid lines that you can use as a scale, you can calculate the **velocity** of the projectile between **different points** in its motion, by looking at how far it travels **between frames**.

A video camera records a series of pictures, or frames (typically around 25 frames per second). Video analysis software lets you view videos frame by frame.

... or **Strobe Photography**

In strobe photography, a camera is set to take a **long exposure**. While the camera is taking the photo, a **strobe light** flashes repeatedly and the projectile is released. The strobe light **lights up** the projectile at regular intervals. This means that the projectile appears **multiple times** in the same photograph, in a **different position** each time.

Again, if you've got a **reference object** in the photo (for example, you might throw an object in front of a **screen** with a **grid** drawn on it), you can calculate **how far** the object travels **between flashes** of the strobe, and use the **time** between flashes to calculate the **velocity** of the projectile between the flashes.

The motion of a typical projectile captured with strobe photography is shown below.

Vertical distance between images is smallest near top of arc (as the object slows down, then turns around and speeds up again).

OBJECT RELEASED

Horizontal distance between images is constant (as horizontal velocity doesn't change).

Strobe photography and video cameras give you more information than using light-gates to study an object's projectile motion. They can be used whatever the size of the object, unlike a light-gate.

Practice Questions

Q1 What is the initial vertical velocity for an object projected horizontally with a velocity of 5 ms^{-1}?

Q2 How does the horizontal velocity of a projectile change with time?

Q3 What is the horizontal component of the velocity of a stone, hurled at 30 ms^{-1} at 35° to the horizontal?

Q4 Explain how you might use video analysis software to analyse the motion of a projectile.

Exam Questions

Q1 Jason stands on a vertical cliff edge throwing stones into the sea below.
He throws a stone horizontally with a velocity of 20 ms^{-1} (to 2 s.f.), 560 m above sea level.

a) Calculate how long it takes for the stone to hit the water from leaving Jason's hand.
Use $g = 9.81$ ms^{-2} and ignore air resistance. [2 marks]

b) Calculate the distance of the stone from the base of the cliff when it hits the water. [2 marks]

Q2 Robin fires an arrow into the air with a vertical velocity of 30.0 ms^{-1}, and a horizontal velocity of 20.0 ms^{-1}, from 1.0 m above horizontal ground. Choose the correct option which shows the maximum height from the ground (to 2 significant figures) reached by his arrow. Use $g = 9.81$ ms^{-2} and ignore air resistance.

A	45 m	C	47 m
B	46 m	D	48 m

[1 mark]

All this physics makes me want to create projectile motions...

...by throwing my revision books out of the window. The maths on these two pages can be tricky, but take it step by step and all will be fine. On the plus side, the next page is full of lovely graphs. Who doesn't love a good graph?

Displacement-Time Graphs

Drawing graphs by hand — oh joy. You'd think examiners had never heard of the graphical calculator.
Ah well, until they manage to drag themselves out of the Dark Ages, you'll just have to grit your teeth and get on with it.

Acceleration Means a Curved Displacement-Time Graph

A graph of displacement against time for an **accelerating object** always produces a **curve**.
If the object is accelerating at a **uniform rate**, then the **rate of change** of the **gradient** will be constant.

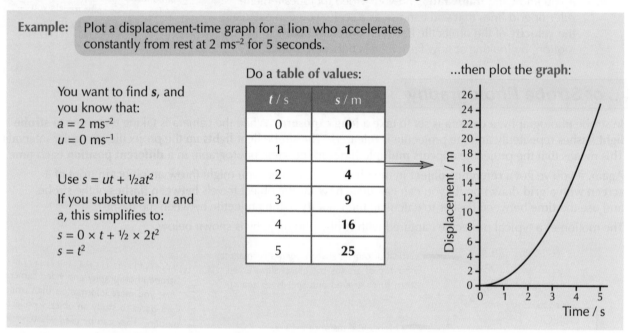

Example: Plot a displacement-time graph for a lion who accelerates constantly from rest at 2 ms⁻² for 5 seconds.

You want to find *s*, and you know that:
$a = 2$ ms⁻²
$u = 0$ ms⁻¹

Use $s = ut + \frac{1}{2}at^2$

If you substitute in *u* and *a*, this simplifies to:
$s = 0 \times t + \frac{1}{2} \times 2t^2$
$s = t^2$

Do a **table of values**:

t / s	s / m
0	0
1	1
2	4
3	9
4	16
5	25

...then plot the **graph**:

Different Accelerations Have Different Gradients

In the example above, if the lion has a **different acceleration** it'll change the **gradient** of the curve like this:

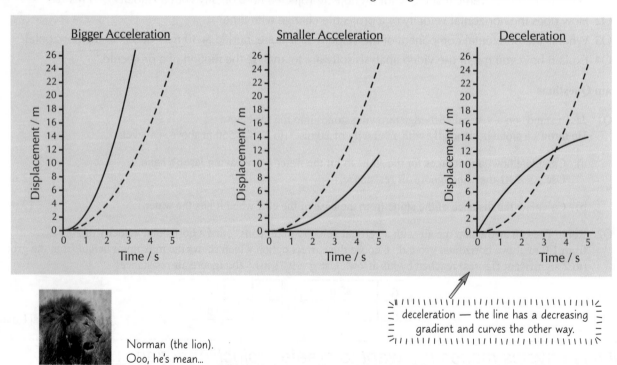

Bigger Acceleration

Smaller Acceleration

Deceleration

Norman (the lion).
Ooo, he's mean...

deceleration — the line has a decreasing
gradient and curves the other way.

Displacement-Time Graphs

*The **Gradient** of a **Displacement-Time Graph** Tells You the Velocity*

When the velocity is constant, the graph's a **straight line**.
Velocity is defined as...

$$\text{velocity} = \frac{\text{change in displacement}}{\text{change in time}}$$

On the graph, this is $\frac{\text{change in } y \, (\Delta y)}{\text{change in } x \, (\Delta x)}$, i.e. the gradient.

So to get the velocity from a displacement-time graph, just find the gradient.

$$v = \frac{\Delta y}{\Delta x}$$
$$= \frac{10}{6} = 1.67 \text{ ms}^{-1}$$

*It's the Same with **Curved Graphs***

If the gradient **isn't constant** (i.e. if it's a curved line), it means the object is **accelerating**.

Acceleration is $\frac{\text{change in velocity} \, (\Delta v)}{\text{change in time} \, (\Delta t)}$, so it is the rate of change of this gradient. If the gradient is constant (straight line) then there is no acceleration, and if it's changing (curved line) then there's acceleration or deceleration.

To find the **instantaneous velocity** at a certain point you need to draw a **tangent** to the curve at that point and find its gradient.

To find the **average velocity** over a period of time, just divide the final (change in) displacement by the final (change in) time — it doesn't matter if the graph is curved or not.

tangent drawn at $t = 5.5$ s

$v = \frac{\Delta y}{\Delta x} = \frac{4}{3} = 1.3 \text{ ms}^{-1}$ (to 2 s.f.) (after 5.5 s)

Practice Questions

Q1 What is given by the slope of a displacement-time graph?

Q2 Sketch a displacement-time graph to show: a) constant velocity,   b) acceleration,   c) deceleration

Exam Questions

Q1 Describe the motion of the cyclist as shown by the graph below.   [4 marks]

Q2 A baby crawls 5 m in 8 seconds at a constant velocity. She then rests for 5 seconds before crawling a further 3 m in 5 seconds at a constant velocity. Finally, she makes her way back to her starting point in 10 seconds, travelling at a constant speed all the way.

a) Draw a displacement-time graph to show the baby's journey.   [4 marks]

b) Calculate her velocity at all the different stages of her journey.   [2 marks]

Be ahead of the curve, get to grips with this stuff now...

Whether it's a straight line or a curve, the steeper it is, the greater the velocity. There's nothing difficult about these graphs — the problem is that it's easy to confuse them with velocity-time graphs (next page). If in doubt, think about the gradient — is it velocity or acceleration, is it changing (curve), is it constant (straight line), is it 0 (horizontal line)...

Velocity-Time and Acceleration-Time Graphs

Speed-time graphs and velocity-time graphs are pretty similar. The big difference is that velocity-time graphs can have a negative part to show something travelling in the opposite direction:

The **Gradient** of a **Velocity-Time Graph** tells you the **Acceleration**

$$\text{acceleration} = \frac{\text{change in velocity}}{\text{time taken}}$$

likewise for a speed-time graph

So the acceleration is just the **gradient** of a **velocity-time graph**.

1) **Uniform** acceleration is always a **straight line**.

2) The **steeper** the **gradient**, the **greater** the **acceleration**.

When the **acceleration** is **constant**, you get a **straight-line** *v-t* graph. The equation for a straight line is $y = mx + c$. You can rearrange the acceleration equation into the same form, getting $v = u + at$. So on a linear *v-t* graph, **acceleration**, *a*, is the **gradient** (*m*) and the **initial speed**, *u*, is the **y-intercept** (*c*).

Example: A lion strolls along at 1.5 ms⁻¹ for 4 s and then accelerates uniformly at a rate of 2.5 ms⁻² for 4 s. Plot this information on a velocity-time graph.

So, for the first four seconds, the velocity is 1.5 ms⁻¹, then it increases by **2.5 ms⁻¹ every second**:

time / s	0-4	5	6	7	8
velocity / ms⁻¹	1.5	4.0	6.5	9.0	11.5

You can see that the **gradient of the line** is **constant** between 4 s and 8 s and has a value of 2.5 ms⁻², representing the **acceleration of the lion**.

$$a = \frac{\Delta v}{\Delta t} = \frac{11.5 - 1.5}{4}$$

$$= 2.5 \text{ ms}^{-2}$$

Acceleration isn't Always **Uniform**

1) If the acceleration is changing, the gradient of the velocity-time graph will also be changing — so you **won't** get a **straight line**.

2) **Increasing acceleration** is shown by an **increasing gradient** — like in curve ①.

3) **Decreasing acceleration** is shown by a **decreasing gradient** — like in curve ②.

Displacement = **Area** under **Velocity-Time Graph**

You know that: | **displacement = velocity × time** |

Similarly, the area under a speed-time graph is the total distance travelled.

The **area** under a velocity-time graph tells you the **displacement** of an object. Areas under any **negative** parts of the graph count as negative areas, as they show the object moving **back** to its **start point**.

Example: A racing car on a straight track accelerates uniformly from rest to 40 ms⁻¹ in 10 s. It maintains this speed for a further 20 s before coming to rest by decelerating at a constant rate over the next 15 s. Draw a velocity-time graph for this journey and use it to calculate the total displacement of the racing car.

Split the **graph** up into **sections**: A, B and C. Calculate the **area** of each and **add** the three results together.

A: Area = ½ base × height = ½ × 10 × 40 = 200 m

B: Area = $b \times h$ = 20 × 40 = 800 m

C: Area = ½ $b \times h$ = ½ × 15 × 40 = 300 m

Total displacement = 1300 m

Velocity-Time and Acceleration-Time Graphs

Acceleration-Time (a-t) Graphs are Useful Too

An **acceleration-time graph** shows how an object's **acceleration** changes over time.

1) The **height** of the graph gives the object's **acceleration** at that time.
2) The **area** under the graph gives the object's **change in velocity**.
3) A negative acceleration is a **deceleration**.
4) If $a = 0$, then the object is moving with **constant velocity**.

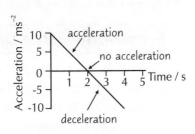

You Have to **Estimate** the Area Under a **Curved** Graph

If an object's acceleration **isn't constant**, you won't get a straight line a-t graph. You need to know how to **estimate** the area under a curved graph. If the graph is on **squared paper**, you can work out the value represented by the **area** of **one** square and multiply by the approximate **number of squares** under the curve. Another way is to split the area approximately into simple shapes, calculate the value of the **area** of each of them, and then **add** them all up.

Example: The acceleration of a car in a drag race is shown in this acceleration-time graph. Calculate its change in velocity.

Change in velocity = area under graph

Split the area under the curve up into trapeziums and a triangle.

0-1 s — estimate the area using a trapezium. Area $= \frac{1}{2}(a + b) \times h$
    a is the length of the first side, $a = 10$
    b is the length of the second side, $b = 9$
    h is the width of each strip, so $h = 1$. Area $= \frac{1}{2}(10 + 9) \times 1 = 9.5$ ms^{-1}

1-2 s — this can also be estimated with another trapezium. $a = 9$, $b = 3.6$, $h = 1$.
    So area $= \frac{1}{2}(9 + 3.6) \times 1 = 6.3$ ms^{-1}

2-3 s — estimated with another trapezium. $a = 3.6$, $b = 0.8$, $h = 1$. So area $= \frac{1}{2}(3.6 + 0.8) \times 1 = 2.2$ ms^{-1}

3-4 s — this estimation uses a triangle. Area $= \frac{1}{2}$(base × height) $= \frac{1}{2}(0.8) \times 1 = 0.4$ ms^{-1}

You can use the same method to find the area under any non-linear graph.

Now add the areas together — Total area $= 9.5 + 6.3 + 2.2 + 0.4 = 18.4$ ms^{-1}
The estimated change in velocity of the car is 18.4 ms^{-1} = **20 ms^{-1} (to 1 s.f.)**

Practice Questions

Q1 How do you calculate acceleration from a velocity-time graph?

Q2 How do you calculate the displacement travelled from a velocity-time graph?

Q3 Sketch velocity-time graphs for constant velocity and constant acceleration.

Q4 Sketch velocity-time and acceleration-time graphs for a boy bouncing on a trampoline.

Q5 What does the area under an acceleration-time graph tell you?

Exam Question

Q1 A skier accelerates uniformly from rest at 2 ms^{-2} down a straight slope for 5 seconds. He then reaches the bottom of the slope and continues along the flat ground, decelerating at 1 ms^{-2} until he stops.

   a) Sketch the velocity-time and acceleration-time graphs for his journey.   [4 marks]

   b) Use your v-t graph from part a) to find the distance travelled by the skier during the first 5 seconds.   [2 marks]

Still awake — I'll give you five more minutes...

There's a really nice sunset outside my window. It's one of those ones that makes the whole landscape go pinky-yellowish. And that's about as much interest as I can muster on this topic. Normal service will be resumed on page 27.

Forces

Remember the vector stuff from the beginning of the section? Good, you're going to need it...

Free-Body Force Diagrams show All Forces on a Single Body

1) **Free-body force** diagrams show a **single body** on its own.

2) The diagram should include all the **forces** that **act on** the body, but **not** the **forces it exerts** on the rest of the world.

3) Remember **forces** are **vector quantities** and so the **arrow labels** should show the **size** and **direction** of the forces.

4) If a body is in **equilibrium** (i.e. not accelerating) the **forces** acting on it will be **balanced**.

Drawing free-body force diagrams isn't too hard — you just need to practise them. Here are a few **examples**:

Gravity pulls apple downwards (weight = m × g, see page 38).

Gravity pulls man down. Air resistance acts to push up on man.

Gravity pulls down on ball. Man pushes down on ball. Earth pushes up on ball.

Hand pushes toy car forward. Friction acts against motion. Gravity pulls down on car. Earth pushes up on car.

If the man is falling at a constant speed, then drag = mg (see p.31).

Resolving a Force means Splitting it into Components

See p.15 for a reminder on resolving vectors.

1) Forces can be in **any direction**, so they're not always at right angles to each other. This is sometimes a bit **awkward** for **calculations**.

2) To make an 'awkward' force easier to deal with, you can think of it as two **separate**, **independent** forces, acting at **right angles** to each other.

The force F has exactly the same effect as the horizontal and vertical forces, F_H and F_V.

Replacing F with F_H and F_V is called **resolving the force F**.

3) These two forces have **no effect** on each other as they are **perpendicular**. E.g. a horizontal force will have no vertical effect, and vice-versa.

4) To find the **size** of a **component** force in a particular **direction**, you need to use trigonometry. Forces are vectors, so you treat them in the same way as velocity or displacement — put them end to end.

So this...   ...could be drawn like this:

Using trigonometry you get:

$$\frac{F_H}{F} = \cos\theta \quad \text{or} \quad F_H = F\cos\theta$$

And:

$$\frac{F_V}{F} = \sin\theta \quad \text{or} \quad F_V = F\sin\theta$$

Remember that $\cos 90° = 0$, so forces which act at an angle of **90°** to each other are **independent** (i.e. they have **no effect** on each other).

Example: A tree trunk is pulled along the ground by an elephant exerting a force of 1200 N at an angle of 25° to the horizontal. Calculate the components of this force in the horizontal and vertical directions.

Horizontal force:
$1200 \times \cos 25° = 1087.5...$
= **1100 N (to 2 s.f.)**

Vertical force:
$1200 \times \sin 25° = 507.1...$
= **510 N (to 2 s.f.)**

Forces

You *Add* the *Components Back Together* to get the *Resultant Force*

1) If **two forces** act on an object, you can find the **resultant** (total) **force** by adding the **vectors** together and creating a **closed triangle**, with the resultant force represented by the **third side**.

2) Forces are vectors (as you know), so use **vector addition** — draw the forces as vector arrows 'tip-to-tail'.

3) Then it's yet more trigonometry and Pythagoras to find the **angle** and the **length** of the third side.

Example: Two dung beetles roll a dung ball along the ground at a constant velocity. Beetle A applies a force of 0.50 N northwards while beetle B exerts a force of 0.20 N eastwards. What is the resultant force on the dung ball?

By Pythagoras, $R^2 = 0.50^2 + 0.20^2 = 0.29$
$R = \sqrt{0.29} = 0.538... = \textbf{0.54 N (to 2 s.f.)}$

$\tan\theta = \dfrac{0.20}{0.50}$ so $\theta = \tan^{-1}\left(\dfrac{0.20}{0.50}\right) = 21.8°... = \textbf{22° (to 2 s.f.)}$

So the resultant force is **0.54 N** at an angle of **22° to the vertical** (i.e. a bearing of 022°).

Choose Sensible *Axes* for *Resolving*

Use directions that **make sense** for the situation you're dealing with. If you've got an object on a slope, choose your directions **along the slope** and **at right angles to it**. You can turn the paper to an angle if that helps.

Always choose sensible axes.

Examiners like to call a slope an "inclined plane".

Example:

The component of the bone's weight down the slope is 2.5 N so you'd need 2.5 N of friction (see p.30) to stop it sliding down.

Practice Questions

Q1 Sketch a free-body force diagram for an ice hockey puck moving horizontally across a flat sheet of ice at a constant speed (assuming it is not being pushed and there is no friction).

Q2 What are the horizontal and vertical components of a force F if it is applied at an angle of θ to the horizontal?

Q3 Use trigonometry to explain why perpendicular components of a force are independent of each other.

Exam Questions

Q1 An 8 kg picture is suspended from a hook as shown in the diagram. Calculate the tension force, T, in the string.

[2 marks]

Q2 Two dogs pull a frisbee as shown in the diagram. Both values given are correct to 3 significant figures. Calculate the resultant force on the frisbee.

[2 marks]

Free-body force diagram — sounds like a dance competition...

Remember those $F\cos\theta$ and $F\sin\theta$ bits. Write them on bits of paper and stick them to your wall. Scrawl them on your pillow. Tattoo them on your brain. Whatever it takes — you just have to learn them.

Newton's Laws of Motion

You did most of this at GCSE, but that doesn't mean you can just skip over it now. You'll be kicking yourself if you forget this stuff in the exam — it's easy marks...

Newton's *1st Law* Says That a **Force** is Needed to Change Velocity

1) **Newton's 1st law of motion** states that the **velocity** of an object will **not change** unless a **resultant force** acts on it.

2) In plain English this means a body will stay still ('at rest') or move in a **straight line** at a **constant speed**, unless there's a **resultant force** acting on it.

An apple sitting on a table won't go anywhere because the **forces** on it are **balanced**.

reaction (*R*)   =   weight (*mg*)
(force of table   (force of gravity
pushing apple up)   pulling apple down,
see p.38)

3) An example of constant velocity is when an object reaches its **terminal velocity** (see p.30). This occurs when the **weight** of a **falling** object is exactly **balanced** by **drag** (e.g. air resistance). Since there is **no resultant force**, there is **no acceleration**, and the object falls at a **constant velocity**.

4) If the forces **aren't balanced**, the **overall resultant force** will make the body **accelerate**. This could be a change in **direction**, or **speed**, or both. (See Newton's 2nd law, below.)

Newton's *2nd Law* Says That *Acceleration* is *Proportional* to the Force

...which can be written as the well-known equation:

resultant force (N) = mass (kg) × acceleration (ms⁻²)

$$\Sigma F = ma$$

The resultant force is the vector sum of all the forces on an object. Σ is the symbol for 'sum of', but you'll often see resultant force as just *F*.

Learn this — it crops up all over the place in Physics. And learn what it means too:

1) It says that the **more force** you have acting on a certain mass, the **more acceleration** you get.

2) It says that for a given force, the **more mass** you have, the **less acceleration** you get.

REMEMBER:
1) The **resultant force** is the **vector sum** of all the forces.
2) The force is **always** measured in **newtons**.
3) The **mass** is always measured in **kilograms** and is a **constant**.
4) The **acceleration** is always in the **same direction** as the **resultant force** and is measured in **ms⁻²**.

3) If you have **no resultant force**, then $\Sigma F = 0$. You can see from $\Sigma F = ma$ that this happens when $a = 0$. And as if by magic (or physics), this **matches** what was said above in Newton's 1st law — **no resultant force** means **no acceleration**.

4) There's more on this most excellent law on p.33.

Galileo said: *All Objects Fall* at the *Same Rate* (if You *Ignore Air Resistance*)

You need to understand **why** this is true. Newton's 2nd law explains it neatly — consider two balls dropped at the same time — ball **1** being heavy, and ball **2** being light. Then use Newton's 2nd law to find their acceleration.

mass = m_1
resultant force = F_1
acceleration = a_1

 W_1

By Newton's Second Law:
$$F_1 = m_1 a_1$$
Ignoring air resistance, the only force acting on the ball is weight, given by $W_1 = m_1 g$ (where g = gravitational field strength = 9.81 Nkg⁻¹).
So: $F_1 = m_1 a_1 = W_1 = m_1 g$
So: $m_1 a_1 = m_1 g$, then m_1 cancels out to give: $a_1 = g$

mass = m_2
resultant force = F_2
acceleration = a_2

 W_2

By Newton's Second Law:
$$F_2 = m_2 a_2$$
Ignoring air resistance, the only force acting on the ball is weight, given by $W_2 = m_2 g$ (where g = gravitational field strength = 9.81 Nkg⁻¹).
So: $F_2 = m_2 a_2 = W_2 = m_2 g$
So: $m_2 a_2 = m_2 g$, then m_2 cancels out to give: $a_2 = g$

...in other words, the **acceleration** is **independent of the mass**. It makes **no difference** whether the ball is **heavy or light**. And I've kindly **hammered home the point** by showing you two almost identical examples.

Newton's Laws of Motion

Newton's *3rd Law* Says Each Force has an *Equal*, *Opposite Reaction Force*

There are a few different ways of stating Newton's 3rd law, but the clearest way is:

> **If an object A exerts a FORCE on object B, then object B exerts AN EQUAL BUT OPPOSITE FORCE on object A.**

You'll also hear the law as "every action has an equal and opposite reaction". But this confuses people who wrongly think the forces are both applied to the same object. (If that were the case, you'd get a resultant force of zero and nothing would ever move anywhere...)

The two forces actually represent the **same interaction**, just seen from two **different perspectives**:

1) If you **push against a wall**, the wall will **push back** against you, **just as hard**. As soon as you stop pushing, so does the wall. Amazing...

2) If you **pull a cart**, whatever force **you exert** on the rope, the rope exerts the **exact opposite** pull on you (unless the rope's stretching).

3) When you go **swimming**, you push **back** against the water with your arms and legs, and the water pushes you **forwards** with an equal-sized force.

Newton's 3rd law applies in **all situations** and to all **types of force**. But the pairs of forces are always the **same type**, e.g. both gravitational or both electrical, and they act along the same line.

This looks like Newton's 3rd law...

Gravity pulls down on book

But it's <u>NOT</u>.

Table pushes upwards on book

...because both forces are acting on the book, and they're not of the same type. They are two separate interactions. The forces are equal and opposite, resulting in zero acceleration, so this is showing Newton's 1st law.

Practice Questions

Q1 State Newton's 1st, 2nd and 3rd laws of motion, and explain what they mean.

Q2 Explain how you can demonstrate Newton's 1st law using Newton's 2nd law.

Q3 What are the two equal and opposite forces acting between an orbiting satellite and the Earth?

Exam Questions

Q1 A boat is moving across a river. The engines provide a force of 500 N at right angles to the flow of the river and the boat experiences a drag of 100 N in the opposite direction. The force on the boat due to the flow of the river is 300 N. The mass of the boat is 250 kg.

a) Calculate the magnitude of the resultant force acting on the boat. [2 marks]

b) Calculate the magnitude of the acceleration of the boat. [1 mark]

Q2 John's bike, which has a mass of m, breaks and he has to push it home. The bike has a constant acceleration a and a frictional force F opposes the motion. What force is John using to push his bike?

A	ma
B	$ma + F$
C	$m(a - F)$
D	$ma - F$

[1 mark]

Q3 Michael and Tom are both keen on diving. They notice that they seem to take the same time to drop from the diving board to the water. Use Newton's second law to explain why this is the case. (Assume no air resistance.) [3 marks]

Newton's three incredibly important laws of motion...

These laws may not really fill you with a huge amount of excitement (and I could hardly blame you if they don't)... but it was pretty fantastic at the time — suddenly people actually understood how forces work, and how they affect motion. I mean arguably it was one of the most important scientific discoveries ever...

Drag and Terminal Velocity

If you jump out of a plane at 1500 m, you want to know that you're not going to be accelerating all the way.

Friction is a Force that Opposes Motion

There are two main types of friction — **friction** between **solid surfaces** and **friction** in a **fluid**. Friction in a fluid is known as **drag** or fluid resistance. **Air resistance** is a type of fluid resistance.

Fluid Friction or Drag:

1) 'Fluid' is a word that means either a **liquid or a gas** — something that can **flow**.

2) The force depends on the thickness (or **viscosity**) of the fluid (see p.64).

3) It **increases** as the **speed increases** (for simple situations it's directly proportional, but you don't need to worry about the mathematical relationship).

4) It also depends on the **shape** of the object moving through it — the larger the **area** pushing against the fluid, the greater the resistance force.

5) A **projectile** (see p.20) is **slowed down** by air resistance. If you calculate how far a projectile will travel without thinking about air resistance, your answer will be **too large**.

Things you need to remember about frictional forces:

1) They **always** act in the **opposite direction** to the **motion** of the object.

2) They can **never** speed things up or start something moving.

3) They convert **kinetic energy** into **heat** and **sound**.

Terminal Velocity — When the Friction Force Equals the Driving Force

You will reach a **terminal (maximum) velocity** at some point, if you have:

1) a **driving force** that stays the **same** all the time

2) a **frictional** or **drag force** (or collection of forces) that increases with velocity

There are **three main stages** to reaching terminal velocity:

The car **accelerates** from **rest** using a constant driving force.	As the **velocity increases**, the **frictional forces increase** (because of things like turbulence — you don't need the details). This **reduces the resultant force** on the car and hence **reduces its acceleration**.	Eventually the car reaches a velocity at which the **frictional forces are equal to the driving force**. There is now **no resultant force** and **no acceleration**, so the car carries on at **constant velocity**.

Different factors affect a vehicle's maximum velocity

As you just saw, a vehicle reaches maximum velocity when the driving force is equal to the frictional force. So there are two main ways of increasing a vehicle's maximum velocity:

1) **Increasing the driving force**, e.g. by increasing the engine size.

2) **Reducing the frictional force**, e.g. making the body more streamlined.

Drag and Terminal Velocity

Things **Falling** through **Air** or **Water** Reach a **Terminal Velocity** too

When something's falling through air, the weight of the object (p.38) is a constant force accelerating the object downwards. Air resistance is a frictional force opposing this motion, which increases with speed.
So before a parachutist opens the parachute, exactly the same thing happens as with the car example:

1) A skydiver leaves a plane and will **accelerate** until the **air resistance** equals his **weight**.

2) He will then be travelling at a **terminal velocity**.

But... the terminal velocity of a person in free fall is too great to land without dying a horrible death.
The **parachute increases** the **air resistance massively**, which slows him down to a lower terminal velocity:

3) Before reaching the ground he will **open his parachute**, which immediately **increases the air resistance** so it is now **bigger** than his **weight**.

4) This **slows him down** until his speed has dropped enough for the **air resistance** to be **equal to his weight** again. This new terminal velocity is small enough for him to land safely.

A *v-t* graph of the skydiver looks like this. He reaches terminal velocity twice during his fall — the second one is much slower than the first.

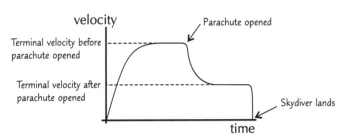

Practice Questions

Q1 What forces limit the velocity of a skier going down a slope?

Q2 Suggest two ways in which the maximum velocity of a car can be increased.

Q3 What conditions cause a terminal velocity to be reached?

Exam Question

Q1 A space probe free-falls towards the surface of a planet.
The graph on the right shows the velocity of the probe as it falls.

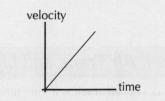

a) The planet does not have an atmosphere. Explain how you can tell this from the graph.   [2 marks]

b) Sketch the velocity-time graph you would expect to see if the planet did have an atmosphere.   [2 marks]

c) Explain the shape of the graph you have drawn.   [3 marks]

You'll never understand this without going parachuting...*

When you're doing questions about terminal velocity, remember the frictional forces reduce acceleration, not speed. They usually don't slow an object down, apart from in the parachute example, where the skydiver is travelling faster just before the parachute opens than the terminal velocity for the open parachute-skydiver combination.

* No. 37 in a series of the 100 least convincing excuses for an interesting holiday.

Momentum

These pages are about linear momentum — that's momentum in a straight line (not a circle).

Understanding **Momentum** Helps You Do **Calculations** for **Collisions**

The **momentum** of an object depends on two things — its **mass** and **velocity**.
The **product** of these two values is the momentum of the object:

$$p = mv$$

where *p* is the momentum in kg ms^{-1},
m is the mass in kg, and *v* is the velocity in ms^{-1}.

*Remember, momentum is a vector quantity, so it has size **and** direction.*

Momentum is Always **Conserved**

You might see momentum referred to as 'linear momentum'. The other kind is 'angular momentum', but you don't need to know about that for now.

1) Assuming **no external forces** act, momentum is always **conserved**.

2) This means the **total momentum** of two objects **before** they collide **equals** the total momentum **after** the collision.

3) This is really handy for working out the **velocity** of objects after a collision (as you do...):

Example: A skater of mass 75 kg and velocity 4.0 ms^{-1} collides with a stationary skater of mass 50 kg (to 2 s.f.). The two skaters join together and move off in the same direction. Calculate their velocity after impact.

4.0 ms^{-1} O ms^{-1} *v* = ?
75 kg   50 kg   125 kg
BEFORE   AFTER

Before you start a momentum calculation, always draw a quick sketch.

Momentum of skaters before = Momentum of skaters after
(75 × 4.0) + (50 × 0) = 125*v*
300 = 125*v*
So *v* = **2.4 ms^{-1}**

4) The same principle can be applied in **explosions**. E.g. if you fire an **air rifle**, the **forward momentum** gained by the pellet **equals** the **backward momentum** of the rifle, and you feel the rifle recoiling into your shoulder.

Example: A bullet of mass 0.0050 kg is shot from a rifle at a speed of 200 ms^{-1} (to 2 s.f.). The rifle has a mass of 4.0 kg. Calculate the velocity at which the rifle recoils.

4.0 kg × *v*   0.0050 kg × 200 ms^{-1}

Momentum before explosion = Momentum after explosion
0 = (0.0050 × 200) + (4.0 × *v*)
0 = 1 + 4*v*
So *v* = **−0.25 ms^{-1}**

An **Air Track** and **Light Gates** are Used to **Investigate** Momentum

1) An **air track** is a long piece of metal with a series of **small holes** along its surfaces. Air is blown through the holes.

2) This air **reduces friction** between the **track** and the **trolleys** that move on top of it.

3) Momentum is only conserved if **no external forces act**, so air tracks are useful for studying conservation of momentum as you can assume there is **no friction**.

4) **Two** trolleys are pushed towards each other on an air track, so that they **collide** between the **light gates**. The light gates measure the **speed** of each trolley as they pass through them.

5) If the speed of each trolley is measured **before** and **after** the collision, the **initial** and **final** momentum of each trolley can be calculated using *p* = *mv*.

light gates

air is blown through holes

air track →

trolleys

Momentum

Newton's 2nd Law *Says That Force is the* **Rate of Change in Momentum**

Newton's second law (p.28) can also be expressed in terms of momentum. The **rate of change of momentum** of an object is **directly proportional** to the **resultant force** which acts on the object.

So: $\boxed{F = \dfrac{\Delta(mv)}{\Delta t}}$ or $\boxed{F\Delta t = \Delta(mv)}$

where F is the resultant force in N,
m is the mass in kg, v is the velocity in ms^{-1},
and t is the time taken for the velocity to change in s.

If the force is changing, F gives the average force over the time interval Δt

Remember that acceleration is equal to the rate of change of velocity (page 16), so if mass is constant then this formula gives you that mechanics favourite, $F = ma$ (or $\Sigma F = ma$) (p.28).

1) You can also relate this formula to **conservation of momentum** by considering **Newton's 3rd law**.

2) If object A **collides** with object B and **exerts** a force F on B for a time Δt, Newton's 3rd law says that object B will also exert a force $-F$ on A for a time Δt.

3) The **change** in A's **momentum** is equal to $-F\Delta t$, and the change in B's momentum is $F\Delta t$, so the **overall** change in momentum is $(-F\Delta t) + F\Delta t = 0$. So momentum is **conserved**.

Example: A snooker ball that is initially at rest is hit with a cue.
The cue is in contact with the ball for 0.0040 s and the speed of the ball immediately after being hit is 0.80 ms^{-1}. The mass of the snooker ball is 0.16 kg.
Calculate the average force exerted on the snooker ball by the cue.

Use the equation $F = \dfrac{\Delta(mv)}{\Delta t}$ and substitute in the values:

$F = \dfrac{\Delta(mv)}{\Delta t} = \dfrac{(0.16 \times 0.80) - (0.16 \times 0)}{0.0040} = \textbf{32 N}$

Practice Questions

Q1 Give two examples of conservation of momentum in practice.

Q2 Explain how light gates and an air track can be used to investigate conservation of momentum.

Q3 Explain how Newton's 2nd law and Newton's 3rd law can be used to demonstrate conservation of momentum.

Exam Questions

Q1 A ball of mass 0.60 kg moving at 5.0 ms^{-1} collides with a larger stationary ball of mass 2.0 kg. The smaller ball rebounds in the opposite direction at 2.4 ms^{-1}.

   a) Calculate the velocity of the larger ball immediately after the collision. [3 marks]

   b) The collision lasts for 0.0055 s. Calculate the average force acting on the smaller ball in this time. [2 marks]

Q2 A toy train of mass 0.7 kg, travelling at 0.3 ms^{-1}, collides with a stationary toy carriage of mass 0.4 kg. The two toys couple together. Calculate their new velocity. [3 marks]

Momentum'll never be an endangered species — it's always conserved...

...unlike record stores, which are quite the opposite and could probably do with your help. You can't match the excitement of running home with a shiny new CD, spending 20 minutes trying to pick through the shrink wrap then sitting back and enjoying 12 glorious new tracks... Speaking of (air) tracks, there's a lot of important stuff here — make sure you know how Newton's laws relate to conservation of momentum.

Work and Power

As everyone knows, work in Physics isn't like normal work. It's harder. Work also has a specific meaning that's to do with movement and forces. You'll have seen this at GCSE — it just comes up in more detail here.

Work is Done Whenever Energy is Transferred

This table gives you some examples of **work being done** and the **energy changes** that happen.

1) Usually you need a force to move something because you're having to **overcome another force**.

2) The thing being moved has **kinetic energy** while it's **moving**.

3) The kinetic energy is transferred to **another form of energy** when the movement stops.

ACTIVITY	WORK DONE AGAINST	FINAL ENERGY FORM
Lifting up a box.	gravity	gravitational potential energy
Pushing a chair across a level floor.	friction	heat
Pushing two magnetic north poles together.	magnetic force	magnetic energy
Stretching a spring.	stiffness of spring	elastic potential energy

The word **'work'** in Physics means the **amount of energy transferred** from one form to another when a force causes a movement of some sort. It's measured in **joules** (J).

Work = Force × Distance

When a car tows a caravan, it applies a force to the caravan to move it to where it's wanted. To **find out** how much **work** has been **done**, you need to use the **equation**:

> **work done (ΔW) = force causing motion (F) × distance moved (Δs), or $\Delta W = F\Delta s$**
>
> ...where ΔW is measured in joules (J), F is measured in newtons (N) and Δs is measured in metres (m).

Points to remember:

1) **Work** is the **energy** that's been **changed** from one form to another — it's not necessarily the **total** energy. E.g. moving a book from a low shelf to a higher one will increase its gravitational potential energy, but it had some potential energy to start with.
   Here, the **work done** would be the **increase** in potential energy, **not the total** potential energy.

2) Remember the distance needs to be measured in metres — if you have a **distance in centimetres or kilometres**, you need to **convert** it to metres first.

3) The force F will be a **fixed** value in any calculations, either because it's **constant** or because it's the **average** force.

4) The equation assumes that the **direction of the force** is the **same** as the **direction of movement**.

5) The equation gives you the **definition** of the joule (symbol J):
   'One joule is the work done when a force of 1 newton moves an object through a distance of 1 metre'.

The Force isn't always in the Same Direction as the Movement

Sometimes the **direction of movement** is **different** from the **direction of the** force.

Example:

1) To **calculate the work done** in a situation like the one on the right, you need to consider the **horizontal** and **vertical components** of the **force**.

2) The only **movement** is in the **horizontal** direction. This means the **vertical force** is not causing any motion (and hence not doing any work) — it's just **balancing** out some of the **weight**, meaning there's a **smaller reaction force**.

direction of force on sledge

rosebud

direction of motion

3) The horizontal force is causing the motion — so to **calculate** the **work done**, this is the **only force** you need to consider. Which means we get:

> $\Delta W = F\Delta s \cos\theta$

Where θ is the **angle** between the **direction of the force** and the **direction of motion**. See page 26 for more on resolving forces.

F

θ

$F\cos\theta$

Direction of motion

Work and Power

Power = Work Done per Second

Power means many things in everyday speech, but in physics (of course!) it has a special meaning. Power is the **rate of doing work** — in other words it is the **amount of energy transferred** from one form to another **per second**. You **calculate power** from the equation:

Power (P) = energy transferred (E) ÷ time (t), or $P = \dfrac{E}{t}$ ...where P is measured in watts (W), E is measured in joules (J) and t is measured in seconds (s).

Since **work done** is **equal** to the **energy transferred**, you can also write this as:

Power (P) = work done (W) ÷ time (t), or $P = \dfrac{W}{t}$ ...where P is measured in watts (W), W is measured in joules (J) and t is measured in seconds (s).

The **watt** (symbol W) is defined as a **rate of energy transfer** equal to **1 joule per second** (Js⁻¹).

Yep, that's more **equations and definitions** for you to **learn**.

> In the equations on this page, W stands for watts (the unit of power) — don't get it confused with W, work done.

Example: A light bulb transfers 230 kJ of electrical energy into light and heat in one hour. Calculate the power of the bulb.

Energy transferred = 230 kJ = 230 000 J

Time taken to transfer the energy = 1 hour = 3600 s

> Remember — 1 kJ = 1000 J

So $P = \dfrac{E}{t} = \dfrac{230\,000}{3600} = 63.888... =$ **64 W (to 2 s.f.)**

Alice always took a long time to transfer any energy.

Practice Questions

Q1 Write down the equation used to calculate work if the force and motion are in the same direction.

Q2 Write down the equation for work if the force is at an angle to the direction of motion.

Q3 Write down the equations relating: a) power and work done   b) power and energy transferred.

Exam Questions

Q1 A traditional narrowboat is drawn by a horse walking along a canal towpath. The horse pulls the boat at a constant speed between two locks which are 1500 m apart. The tension in the rope is 100 N at 40° to the direction of motion.

a) Calculate the work done on the boat. [2 marks]

b) It take 31 minutes for the horse to pull the boat between the two locks. Calculate the power supplied to the boat. [2 marks]

Q2 A motor is used to lift a 20.0 kg load a height of 3.0 m. ($g = 9.81$ ms⁻²)

a) Calculate the work done in lifting the load. [2 marks]

b) The speed of the load as it is lifted is 0.25 ms⁻¹. Calculate the power delivered by the motor. [3 marks]

Work — there's just no getting away from it...

Loads of equations to learn. Well, that's what you came here for, after all. Can't beat a good bit of equation-learning, as I've heard you say quietly to yourself when you think no one's listening. Aha, can't fool me. Ahahahahahahahahaha.

Conservation of Energy and Efficiency

Energy cannot be created or destroyed (don't forget that). Which is basically what I'm about to take up two whole pages saying. But that's, of course, because you need to do exam questions on this as well as understand the principle.

Learn the **Principle** of **Conservation** of **Energy**

The **principle of conservation of energy** says that:

> Energy **cannot be created** or **destroyed**. Energy **can be transferred** from one form to another but the total amount of energy in a closed system will not change.

Total energy in = Total energy out

Greg started panic-buying when he heard that more energy couldn't be created.

You need it for **Questions** about **Kinetic** and **Potential Energy**

The principle of conservation of energy nearly always comes up when you're doing questions about **changes** between **kinetic** and **potential energy**. A quick reminder:

1) **Kinetic energy** is the energy of anything due to its **motion**, which you work out from: $E_K = \frac{1}{2}mv^2$ — *m* is the mass of the object (kg) and *v* is its velocity (ms⁻¹)

2) There are **different types of potential energy** — e.g. gravitational potential energy and elastic strain (see page 58).

3) **Gravitational potential energy** is the energy something gains if you lift it up. The **equation** for the change in gravitational potential energy close to the **Earth's surface** is:

> change in gravitational potential energy = $\Delta E_{grav} = mg\Delta h$ — *g* is the acceleration due to gravity, $g = 9.81$ ms⁻² and Δh is the change in height (m)

Example: A pendulum has a mass of 700 g and a length of 50 cm. It is pulled out to an angle of 30° from the vertical.

a) Find the gravitational potential energy stored in the pendulum bob.

Start by drawing a diagram.
You can work out the increase in height, Δh, of the end of the pendulum using trig.
$\Delta E_{grav} = mg\Delta h = 0.7 \times 9.81 \times (0.5 - 0.5\cos30°) = 0.460... = $ **0.5 J (to 1 s.f.)**

b) The pendulum is released. Find the maximum speed of the pendulum bob as it passes the vertical position. Assume there is no air resistance.

When travelling at its maximum speed, all of the gravitational potential energy has been transferred to kinetic energy, so $mg\Delta h = \frac{1}{2}mv^2 = 0.460...$

$\frac{1}{2}mv^2 = 0.460...$, so $v = \sqrt{\frac{2 \times 0.460...}{0.7}} = 1.146... = $ **1 ms⁻¹ (to 1 s.f.)**

Or, you could cancel the '*m*'s and rearrange to give: $v = \sqrt{2g\Delta h}$
$= \sqrt{2 \times 9.81 \times (0.5 - 0.5\cos30°)}$
$= $ **1 ms⁻¹ (to 1 s.f.)**

Conservation of Energy and Efficiency

All Energy Transfers Involve Losses

You saw on the last page that **energy can never be created or destroyed**. But whenever **energy** is **converted** from one form to another, some is always **'lost'**. It's still there (i.e. it's **not destroyed**) — it's just not in a form you can **use**.

Most often, **energy** is lost as **heat** — e.g. **computers** and **TVs** are always **warm** when they've been on for a while. In fact, **no device** (except possibly a heater) is ever **100% efficient** (see below) because some energy is **always** lost as **heat**. (You want heaters to give out heat, but in other devices the heat loss isn't useful.) Energy can be **lost** as other forms too (e.g. **sound**) — the important thing is the lost energy **isn't** in a **useful** form and you **can't** get it back.

Energy is often lost as **heat** due to **friction**. For example, imagine pushing a **box** along a **table**. **Frictional forces** between the box and the table surface act in the **opposite direction** to the **motion** of the box (see p.30). Work has to be done to **overcome** this friction — energy is transferred to **heat**. Luckily you can usually assume that **friction** is **zero** in exams.

Efficiency is the Ratio of Useful Energy Output to Total Energy Input

Efficiency is one of those words we use all the time, but it has a **specific meaning** in Physics. It's a measure of how well a **device** converts the **energy** you put **in** into the energy you **want** it to give **out**. So, a device that **wastes** loads of **energy** as heat and sound has a really **low efficiency**.

$$\text{Efficiency} = \frac{\text{useful energy output}}{\text{total energy input}} \quad \text{Or} \quad \text{Efficiency} = \frac{\text{useful power output}}{\text{total power input}}$$

You can multiply either of these equations by 100 to find the efficiency as a percentage.

Some questions will be kind and **give you** the **useful output energy** — others will tell you how much is **wasted**. You just have to **subtract** the **wasted energy** from the **total input energy** to find the **useful output energy**, so it's not too tricky if you keep your wits about you.

Energy, as always, is measured in joules (J). Efficiency has no units because it's a fraction (or a percentage).

Practice Questions

Q1 State the principle of conservation of energy.

Q2 Show that, if there's no air resistance and the mass of the string is negligible, the speed of a pendulum is independent of the mass of the bob.

Q3 Why can a device never be 100% efficient?

Q4 Give an equation for efficiency in terms of a) energy and b) power.

Exam Questions

acceleration of free fall, g = 9.81 ms⁻²

Q1 A skateboarder is skating on a half-pipe. He lets the board run down one side of the ramp and up the other. The height of the ramp is 2.0 m.

  a) Calculate his speed at the lowest point of the ramp. Assume friction is negligible. [3 marks]

  b) State how high he will rise up the other side of the half-pipe. [1 mark]

  c) Real ramps are not frictionless. Describe what the skater must do to reach the top on the other side. [1 mark]

Q2 A 20.0 g rubber ball is released from a height of 8.0 m. Assume that the effect of air resistance is negligible.

  a) Calculate the kinetic energy of the ball just before it hits the ground. [2 marks]

  b) The ball strikes the ground and rebounds to a height of 6.5 m. Calculate the amount of energy that is converted to heat and sound in the impact with the ground. [2 marks]

Q3 Calculate the efficiency (as a fraction) of a device that wastes 65 J for every 140 J of input energy. [1 mark]

Eat, sleep, state the principle of conservation of energy, repeat...

Remember to check your answers — I can't count the number of times I've forgotten to square the velocities or to multiply by the ½... I reckon it's definitely worth the extra minute to check. You never know what you might find.

Mass, Weight and Centre of Gravity

I'm sure you know all this 'mass', 'weight' and 'centre of gravity' stuff from GCSE. But let's just make sure...

The Mass of a Body makes it Resist Changes in Motion

1) The **mass** of an object is the **amount of 'stuff'** (or **matter**) in it. It's measured in **kg**.

2) The greater an object's mass, the greater its **resistance** to a **change in velocity**.

3) The **mass** of an object **doesn't change** if the strength of the **gravitational field** changes.

4) As you've already seen in this topic, weight is a **force**. It's measured in **newtons** (N), like all forces.

5) Weight is the **force experienced by a mass** due to a **gravitational field**.

6) The weight of an object **does vary** according to the size of the **gravitational field** acting on it.

> The value of $g = 9.81$ Nkg^{-1} is only true close to the Earth's surface (p.18).

weight = mass × gravitational field strength ($W = mg$) where $g = 9.81$ Nkg^{-1} on Earth.

This table shows a lion's mass and weight on the Earth and the Moon.

Name	Quantity	Earth ($g = 9.81$ Nkg^{-1})	Moon ($g = 1.6$ Nkg^{-1})
Mass	Mass (scalar)	150 kg	150 kg
Weight	Force (vector)	1470 N (to 3 s.f.)	240 N (to 2 s.f.)

Weight 240 N

Weight 1470 N

Centre of Gravity — Assume All the Mass is in One Place

1) The **centre of gravity** of an object is the **single point** that you can consider its **whole weight** to **act through** (whatever its orientation).

2) The object will always **balance** around this **point**, although in some cases the **centre of gravity** will **fall outside** the object.

> You might come across the phrase 'extended body' when dealing with the centre of gravity. This is just another name for an object that isn't a single point.

Centre of gravity

Centre of gravity

Centre of gravity

Find the Centre of Gravity either by Symmetry...

1) To find the centre of gravity for a **regular** object you can just use **symmetry**.

2) The centre of gravity of any regular shape is at its **centre** — where the lines of symmetry will cross.

3) The centre of gravity is **halfway** through the **thickness** of the object at the point the lines meet.

Centre of gravity

The symmetry in this picture shows the centre of cuteness.

Mass, Weight and Centre of Gravity

... Or By Experiment

Experiment to find the Centre of Gravity of an Irregular Object

1) **Hang** the object freely from a point (e.g. one corner).
2) Draw a **vertical line** downwards from the point of suspension — use a plumb bob to get your line exactly vertical.
3) Hang the object from a different point.
4) Draw another vertical line down.
5) The centre of gravity is where the two lines **cross**.

A plumb bob is just a weight on a string — when suspended, the string will be exactly vertical.

How High the Centre of Gravity is tells you How Stable the Object is

1) An object will be nice and **stable** if it has a **low centre** of gravity and a **wide base area**. This idea is used a lot in design, e.g. racing cars.

2) The **higher** the **centre of gravity**, and the **smaller** the **base area**, the **less stable** the object will be. Think of unicyclists...

3) An object will topple over if a **vertical line** drawn **downwards** from its **centre of gravity** falls **outside** its **base area**. This is because the object's weight is causing a turning force (a moment — see p.40) around a pivot.

The vertical line is the line of action of the weight — see next page.

Practice Questions

Q1 A lioness has a mass of 200 kg. What would be her mass and weight on Earth and on the Moon (where $g = 1.6$ Nkg^{-1})?

Q2 Define centre of gravity.

Exam Questions

Q1 Joanne weighs X N on Earth. Which of the following statements are correct?

  A She will weigh the same on the Moon as on Earth.

  B Her mass is equal to $\frac{X}{g}$ kg.

  C Her mass depends on the gravitational field strength.

  D Her acceleration due to gravity will be the same on Earth as the Moon. [1 mark]

Q2 a) Describe an experiment to find the centre of gravity of an object of uniform density with a constant thickness and irregular cross-section. [3 marks]

  b) Identify one major source of uncertainty for this method and suggest a way to reduce its effect on the accuracy of the result. [2 marks]

The centre of gravity of this book should be round about page 50...

This is a really useful area of physics. To would-be nuclear physicists it might seem a little dull, but if you want to be an engineer — then things like centre of gravity and weight are dead important things to understand. You know, for designing things like cars and submarines... yep, pretty useful I'd say.

Moments

*This is not a time for jokes. There is not a moment to lose. Oh ho ho ho ho *bang*. (Ow.)*

A **Moment** is the **Turning Effect** of a **Force**

The **moment** of a **force** depends on the **size** of the force and **how far** the force is applied from the **turning point** (also called the **axis of rotation**):

The line of action of a force is a line along which it acts.

moment of a force (in Nm) = **force** (in N) × **perpendicular distance from the line of action of the force to the axis of rotation** (in m)

$$M = Fx$$

Moments Must be **Balanced** or the **Object** will **Turn**

The **principle of moments** states that for a body to be in **equilibrium**, the **sum of the clockwise moments** about any point **equals** the **sum of the anticlockwise moments** about the same point.

Remember $\sum$ means "the sum of".

Example:

Two children sit on a seesaw as shown in the diagram. An adult balances the seesaw at one end. Find the size and direction of the force that the adult needs to apply.

In equilibrium, $\sum$ anticlockwise moments = $\sum$ clockwise moments

$$400 \times 1.5 = (300 \times 1.0) + 1.5F$$
$$600 = 300 + 1.5F$$

Final answer: F = **200 N downwards**

400 N   1.5 m   1.0 m   0.5 m   300 N

Muscles, **Bones** and **Joints** Act as **Levers**

1) In a lever, an **effort force** (in this case from a muscle) acts against a **load force** (e.g. the weight of your arm) by means of a **rigid object** (the bone) rotating around a **pivot** (the joint).

2) You can use the **principle of moments** to answer lever questions:

Example:

Find the force, E, exerted by the biceps in holding a bag of gold still. The bag of gold weighs 100 N and the forearm weighs 20 N.

Take moments about **A**.
In equilibrium:

$$\sum \text{anticlockwise moments} = \sum \text{clockwise moments}$$
$$(100 \times 0.4) + (20 \times 0.2) = 0.04E$$
$$40 + 4 = 0.04E$$

Final answer: E = 1100 = **1000 N (to 1 s.f.)**

Effort from biceps, E, 40 cm, 20 cm, A, 4 cm, 100 N, 20 N

The Principle of Moments can **Explain** why Things **Fall Over**

1) As you saw on page 39, you can assume that **all** the weight of an object **acts through** its **centre of gravity**. This is important when dealing with moments.

2) Imagine you are trying to balance a broomstick on a pivot. If the **centre of gravity** is to one side of the **pivot** (as shown here) then there will be a **clockwise** moment due to the **weight** of the broomstick acting at a **distance x** from the pivot. There is **no anticlockwise** moment, so the broomstick will **rotate** clockwise (fall off the pivot).

3) However, if the centre of gravity is **directly above** the pivot, then there are no clockwise or anticlockwise **moments** and so the broomstick is in **equilibrium**.

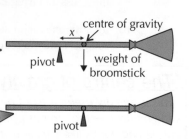

centre of gravity, x, pivot, weight of broomstick, pivot

Moments

*Sometimes you Need to **Resolve Forces** to Calculate **Moments***

Example:

Jamie Band is trying to save some top secret documents falling from a plank which is hanging precariously over a cliff. The diagram shows the plank pivoting at the edge of the cliff, labelled point P. He has tied a rope to one end of the plank and attached the other end of the rope to the ground. Jamie edges towards the top secret documents, but gets scared and stops at the point shown in the diagram below. Jamie has a mass of 75 kg and the top secret documents have a mass of 12 kg.

The distances and angles have been drawn to scale on the diagram below. Assuming the mass of the plank is negligible, calculate the tension, *T*, in the rope.

First you need to resolve all the forces (see p.26) acting perpendicular to the plank by measuring the angle between the line of action of Jamie's weight and the plank.

Angle $\theta = 60°$, so the force exerted by Jamie's weight acting perpendicular to the plank = $m_{Jamie}g \times \sin60°$ and the force exerted by the documents acting perpendicular to the plank = $m_{doc}g \times \sin60°$.

The angle between the rope and plank is 90°, so the tension acting perpendicular to the plank is just *T*.

Remember — the force due to gravity of an object is its weight, where $W = mg$ (see p.38).

You then need to measure all the distances: from P to rope = 3.6 cm, from P to Jamie = 1.2 cm, from P to documents = 2.8 cm. Using these values and the values for the forces, you can use the principle of moments to give:

Σ anticlockwise moments = Σ clockwise moments

$T \times 3.6 = (m_{Jamie}g \times \sin60° \times 1.2) + (m_{doc}g \times \sin60° \times 2.8)$

Which gives: $T = \dfrac{(75 \times 9.81 \times \sin60° \times 1.2) + (12 \times 9.81 \times \sin60° \times 2.8)}{3.6} = 291.68... = \textbf{290 N (to 2 s.f.)}$

Practice Questions

Q1 A force of 54 N acts at a perpendicular distance of 84 cm from a pivot. Calculate the moment of the force.

Q2 A girl of mass 40 kg sits 1.5 m from the middle of a seesaw.
Show that her brother, mass 50 kg, must sit 1.2 m from the middle if the seesaw is to balance.

Q3 Explain why a ruler will only balance on a narrow pivot if it is positioned so the pivot is exactly halfway along the ruler.

Exam Questions

Q1 A driver is changing his flat tyre. The moment required to undo the nut is 60 Nm (to 2 s.f.).
He uses a 0.40 m long spanner. Calculate the force that he must apply at the end of the spanner. [2 marks]

Q2 A diver of mass 60 kg stands on the end of a diving board 2.0 m from the pivot point.
Calculate the downward force exerted on the board by the retaining spring 30 cm from the pivot.

pivot

[2 marks]

It's all about balancing — just ask a tightrope walker...

They're always boring questions aren't they — seesaws or bicycles. It'd be nice if just once, they'd have a question on... I don't know, rotating knives or something. Just something unexpected. It'd make physics a lot more fun, I'm sure.

Charge, Current and Potential Difference

Electricity's brilliant, I love it. It's what gets me out of bed in the morning. (Not literally of course, that'd be quite painful.)

Current is the Rate of Flow of Charge

1) The **current** in a **wire** is like **water** flowing in a **pipe**. The **amount** of water that flows depends on the **flow rate** and the **time**. It's the same with electricity — **current is the rate of flow of charge**.

$$I = \frac{\Delta Q}{\Delta t}$$
Where I is the current in amperes, ΔQ is the charge in coulombs, and Δt is the time taken in seconds.

Remember that conventional current flows from + to −, the opposite way from electron flow.

2) The **coulomb** is the **unit of charge**.

> **One coulomb** (C) is defined as the **amount of charge** that passes in **1 second** when the **current** is **1 ampere**.

3) You can measure the current flowing through part of a circuit using an **ammeter**. This is the circuit symbol for an ammeter:

Attach an ammeter in series with the component you're investigating.

Potential Difference is the Work Done per Unit Charge

1) To make electric charge flow through a conductor, you need to do **work** on it.

2) **Potential difference** (p.d.), or **voltage**, is defined as the **work done per unit charge moved**:

$$V = \frac{W}{Q}$$
W is the work done in joules (see p.34). It's the energy transferred in moving the charge.

> The **potential difference** across a component is **1 volt** (V) when you do **1 joule** of work moving **1 coulomb** of charge through the component. This **defines** the volt.

$$1\,V = 1\,J\,C^{-1}$$

Back to the 'water analogy' again. The p.d. is like the pressure that's forcing water along the pipe.

Resistor 6V

Here you do 6 J of work moving each coulomb of charge through the resistor, so the p.d. across it is 6 V. The energy gets converted to heat.

3) You can measure the potential difference across a component using a **voltmeter**. This is the circuit symbol for a voltmeter:

4) Remember, the potential difference across components in parallel is **the same**, so the **voltmeter** should be connected in **parallel** with the component you're investigating.

The maximum value that a voltmeter or ammeter can measure is called the full scale deflection.

Charge Carriers in Liquids and Gases are Ions

1) A current is the **rate of flow of charged particles** (called **charge carriers**). In a circuit, the charge carriers are free electrons (sometimes called **conduction electrons**), but there are **other types** of charge carrier.

2) A flow of **positively-charged** particles produces **exactly** the **same current** as an **equal** flow of negatively-charged particles in the **opposite direction**. This is why we use **conventional current**, defined as 'in the same direction as a flow of positive charges'.

3) **Ionic crystals** like sodium chloride are **insulators**. Once **molten**, though, the liquid **conducts**. Positive and negative **ions** are the **charge carriers**. The **same thing** happens in an **ionic solution** like copper sulfate solution.

4) **Gases** are **insulators**, but if you apply a **high enough voltage** electrons get **ripped out** of **atoms**, giving you **ions** along a path. You get a **spark**.

Uses of ions in air include creating a dramatic backdrop to a Gothic horror story, and bringing the creations of mad scientists to life.

Charge, Current and Potential Difference

The *Mean Drift Velocity* is the *Average* Velocity of the *Charge Carriers*

When **current** flows through a wire, you might imagine the **electrons** all moving uniformly in the **same direction**. In fact, they move **randomly** in **all directions**, but tend to **drift** one way. The **mean drift velocity** is just the **average velocity** and it's **much, much less** than the electrons' **actual speed**. (Their actual speed is about 10^6 ms^{-1}.)

The Current Depends on the Mean Drift Velocity:

The charge on an electron, e, is -1.60×10^{-19} C.

The **current** is given by the equation:

$$I = nqvA$$

where: I = electrical current (A)
n = number density of charge carriers (m^{-3}) (number per unit volume)
q = charge on each charge carrier (C)
v = mean drift velocity (ms^{-1})
A = cross-sectional area (m^2)

So...

1) Double the number of charge carriers and the current doubles.

2) If the carriers move twice as fast you get twice the charge in the same time — twice the current.

3) Doubling the area also doubles the current.

4) Doubling the charge carried by each carrier gives you twice the charge in the same time — twice the current.

Different Materials have Different Numbers of *Charge Carriers*

1) In a **metal**, the **charge carriers** are **free electrons** — they're the ones from the **outer shell** of each atom. Thinking about the formula $I = nqvA$, there are **loads** of charge carriers per unit volume, making n **big**. The **drift velocity** is **small**, even for a **high current**.

2) **Semiconductors** have **fewer charge carriers**, so the **drift velocity** needs to be **higher** to give the **same current**.

3) A **perfect insulator** wouldn't have **any charge carriers**, so $n = 0$ in the formula and you'd get **no current**. Real insulators have a **very small** n.

Practice Questions

Q1 Describe in words and symbols how current and charge are related.
Q2 Define potential difference.
Q3 What happens to the current in a wire if the mean drift velocity of the electrons is halved?
Q4 Describe how metals, semiconductors and insulators differ in terms of n.

Exam Questions

Q1 A battery delivers 4500 C of electric charge to a circuit in 10 minutes. Calculate the average current. [1 mark]

Q2 A kettle runs off the mains supply (230 V) and has an overall efficiency of 88%. Calculate how much electric charge will pass through the kettle if it transfers 308 J of energy to the water it contains. [2 marks]

Q3 Copper has 1.0×10^{29} free electrons per m^3. Calculate the mean drift velocity of the electrons in a copper wire of cross-sectional area 5.0×10^{-6} m^2 when it is carrying a current of 13 A. [2 marks]

I can't even be bothered to make the current joke...

Talking of currant jokes, I saw this bottle of wine the other day called 'raisin d'être' — 'raison d'être' meaning 'reason for living', but spelled slightly differently to make 'raisin', meaning 'grape'. Ho ho. Chuckled all the way home.

Resistance and Resistivity

Resistance and resistivity. Not quite the same word, not quite the same thing. Make sure you know which is which...

Everything has Resistance

1) If you put a **potential difference** (p.d.) across an **electrical component**, a **current** will flow.
2) **How much** current you get for a particular **p.d.** depends on the **resistance** of the component.
3) You can think of a component's **resistance** as a **measure** of how **difficult** it is to get a **current** to **flow** through it.

Mathematically, **resistance** is:
This equation really **defines** what is meant by resistance.

$$R = \frac{V}{I}$$

This is the **circuit symbol** for a resistor:

4) **Resistance** is measured in **ohms** (Ω).

A component has a resistance of **1 Ω** if a **potential difference** of **1 V** makes a **current** of **1 A** flow through it.

Three Things Determine Resistance

If you think about a nice, **simple electrical component**, like a **length of wire**, its **resistance** depends on:

1) **Length (*l*).** The **longer** the wire the **more difficult** it is to make a **current flow**.
2) **Area (*A*).** The **wider** the wire the **easier** it is to make a current flow.
3) **Resistivity (*ρ*).** This **depends** on the **material** the wire's made from, as the **structure** of the material may make it easy or difficult for charge to flow. In general, resistivity depends on **environmental factors** as well, like **temperature**.

ρ is the Greek letter rho, the symbol for resistivity.

The **resistivity** of a material is defined as the **resistance** of a **1 m length** with a **1 m² cross-sectional area**, so $\rho = \frac{RA}{l}$. Resistivity is measured in **ohm metres** (Ωm).

In your exams, you'll be given this equation in the **form**:
Typical values for the **resistivity** of **conductors** are **really small**.
However, if you **calculate** a **resistance** for a **conductor** and end up with something **really small** (e.g. 1 × 10⁻⁷ Ω), go back and **check** that you've **converted** your **area** into **m²**.

$$R = \frac{\rho l}{A}$$

where *A* = cross-sectional area in m², and *l* = length in m

The resistivity of a material is related to the **number density of charge carriers**, (and their **mean drift velocity**, which often varies with temperature, p.46). The higher the number of charge carriers, (and the higher their mean drift velocity), the higher the current at a given p.d. (as ***I = nqvA***, see p.43), and so the lower the resistance and therefore the lower the material's resistivity.

The number density of charge carriers **varies greatly** between different materials (see p.43), which means there can be a **huge variation** in their resistivities.

For an Ohmic Conductor, R is a Constant

A chap called **Ohm** did most of the early work on resistance. He developed a rule to **predict** how the **current** would **change** as the applied **potential difference increased**, for **certain types** of conductor.

The rule is now called **Ohm's law** and the conductors that **obey** it (mostly metals) are called **ohmic conductors**.

Provided the **temperature** is **constant**, the **current** through an ohmic conductor is **directly proportional** to the **potential difference** across it (that's ***I ∝ V***).

1) As you can see from the graph, **doubling** the **p.d. doubles** the **current**.
2) What this means is that the **resistance** is **constant**.
3) Often **external factors**, such as **temperature** will have a **significant effect** on resistance, so you need to remember that Ohm's law is **only** true for **ohmic conductors** at constant temperature.

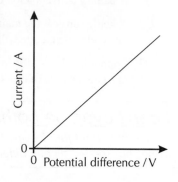

Resistance and Resistivity

To Find the Resistivity of a Wire You Need to Find its Resistance

Before you start, you need to know the **cross-sectional area** of your test wire.
Assume that the wire is **cylindrical**, and so the cross-section is **circular**.

Then you can find its **cross-sectional area** using: | **area of a circle = πr^2** |

Use a **micrometer** to measure the **diameter** of the test wire for at least **three**
different points along the wire. Take an **average** value of the diameter and
divide by **2** to get the **radius** (make sure this is in m). Plug it into the equation for
cross-sectional area and... **ta da**. Now you can get your teeth into the electricity bit...

A micrometer, sometimes called a micrometer caliper, is used to precisely measure very small distances.

1) The **test wire** should be **clamped** to a ruler and connected to
   the rest of the circuit at the point where the ruler reads zero.

2) Attach the **flying lead** to the test wire — the lead is
   just a wire with a crocodile clip at the end to allow
   connection to any point along the test wire.

3) Record the **length** of the test wire **connected** in the circuit,
   the **voltmeter reading** and the **ammeter reading**.

4) Use your readings to calculate the
   resistance of the length of wire, using: ⟹ | $R = \dfrac{V}{I}$ |

5) Repeat for several **different** lengths within
   a sensible range, e.g. at 0.10 m intervals
   from 0.10 m to 1.00 m.

6) Plot your results on a graph of **resistance** against
   length, and draw a **line of best fit** (see page 8).

You could also use a digital multimeter to measure the resistance of the wire directly — you'd connect it in parallel with the length of wire you're investigating and set it to measure resistance.

The **gradient** of the line of best fit is equal to $\dfrac{R}{l} = \dfrac{\rho}{A}$. So **multiply** the **gradient** of the line
of best fit by the **cross-sectional area** of the wire to find the resistivity of the wire material.

7) The **resistivity** of a material depends on its **temperature**, so you can only find the resistivity of a material **at a
   certain temperature**. Current flowing in the test wire can cause its temperature to increase, so failing to keep
   the wire at a **constant temperature** could invalidate your results (see p.12). Try to keep the temperature of the
   test wire constant by e.g. only having small currents flow through the wire.

Practice Questions

Q1 State the equation that links the resistance of a wire to its resistivity.

Q2 The resistivity of a piece of glass is 1×10^{11} Ωm at 20 °C. The resistivity of aluminium at 20 °C is around
3×10^{-8} Ωm. Explain this difference in terms of charge carriers.

Q3 What is Ohm's law?

Q4 Describe an experiment to find the resistivity of a metal.

Exam Questions

Q1 Aluminium has a resistivity of 2.8×10^{-8} Ω m at 20 °C.
Calculate the resistance of a pure aluminium wire of length 4.0 m and diameter 1.0 mm, at 20 °C. [3 marks]

Q2 The table on the right shows some measurements taken by a student
during an experiment investigating an unknown electrical component.
The temperature of the circuit is held constant throughout the experiment.

P.d. / V	3.00	7.00	11.00
Current /mA	4.00	9.33	14.67

a) Calculate the resistance of the component when a p.d. of 7.00 V is applied. [1 mark]

b) State whether the component is an ohmic conductor. Explain your answer. [3 marks]

I find the resistivity to my chat-up lines is very high...

*Examiners love to ask questions about this experiment, so make sure you learn it well. Make sure you can think of some
ways to reduce random errors too — e.g. by repeating measurements and by using more sensitive equipment.*

I-V Characteristics

Woohoo — real physics. This stuff's actually kind of interesting.

I-V Graphs Show How Resistance Varies

Make sure you learn all the circuit symbols that come up in this section, and know how to design and use circuits using them.

The term '*I-V characteristic*' refers to a **graph** which shows how the **current** (I) flowing through a **component changes** as the **potential difference** (V) across it is increased.

You can investigate the *I-V* characteristic of a component using a **test circuit** like this one:

1) Use the **variable resistor** to alter the **potential difference** across the component and the **current** flowing through it, and record V and I.

2) **Repeat** your measurements and take **averages** to reduce the effect of random errors on your results.

3) **Plot a graph** of current against potential difference from your results. This graph is the *I-V* **characteristic** of the component.

variable resistor.

The I-V Characteristic for a Metallic Conductor is a Straight Line

1) At **constant temperature**, the **current** through a **metallic conductor**, e.g. a **wire** or a **resistor**, is **directly proportional** to the **potential difference**.

2) The fact that the characteristic graph is a **straight line through the origin** tells you that the **resistance doesn't change** — it's equal to 1 / gradient.

3) The **shallower** the **gradient** of the characteristic *I-V* graph, the **greater** the **resistance** of the conductor.

4) **Metallic conductors** are **ohmic** — they have **constant resistance provided** their temperature doesn't change (see below).

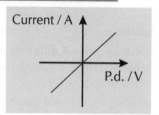

The I-V Characteristic for a Filament Lamp is Curved

Filament lamp circuit symbol:

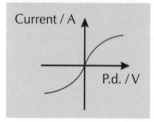

1) The characteristic graph for a **filament lamp** is a **curve**, which starts **steep** but gets **shallower** as the **potential difference rises**.

2) The **filament** in a lamp is just a **coiled up** length of **metal wire**, so you might think it should have the **same characteristic graph** as a **metallic conductor**.

3) However, **current** flowing through the lamp **increases** its **temperature**, so its **resistance increases** (see below).

The Resistivity of a Metal Increases with Temperature

1) **Charge** is carried through **metals** by **free electrons** in a **lattice** of **positive ions**.

2) Heating up a metal makes it **harder** for electrons to **move about**. The **lattice of ions vibrates more** when heated, meaning the electrons **collide** with them more frequently, **transferring** some of their **kinetic energy** into other forms.

ion
electron

3) When kinetic energy is **lost** by the individual electrons, their speed and therefore the **mean drift velocity** (see page 43) decreases. As current is proportional to drift velocity, ($I = nqvA$) this means the **current** in the wire **decreases** so its **resistance** (and its resistivity, as it's dimensions haven't changed) **increases**.

Semiconductors are Used in Sensors

1) **Semiconductors** have a **higher resistivity** than **metals** because there are fewer **charge carriers** available (see page 43).

2) However, if **energy** is supplied to some types of semiconductor (e.g. by increasing their temperature), **more charge carriers** are **released**, so the current increases (as $I = nqvA$) and their resistance and resistivity **decrease**.

Like metals, increasing the temperature of semiconductors increases their lattice vibrations, reducing the mean drift velocity of electrons. But this effect is dwarfed by the effect of releasing more charge carriers with increasing temperature.

3) This means that they can make **excellent sensors** for detecting **changes** in their **environment**. You need to know about **three** semiconductor components — **thermistors**, **LDRs** and **diodes** (see the next page).

I-V Characteristics

The **Resistance** of a **Thermistor** Depends on **Temperature**

A **thermistor** is a **resistor** with a **resistance** that depends on its **temperature**. You only need to know about **NTC** thermistors — NTC stands for 'Negative Temperature Coefficient'. This means that the **resistance decreases** as the **temperature goes up**.

Thermistor circuit symbol:

The resistance of an NTC thermistor **decreases** with **temperature**.

The characteristic **I-V graph** for an NTC thermistor looks like this: As the voltage **increases**, the current **increases**. More current leads to an **increase in temperature** and so a **decrease in resistance**. This in turn means more current can flow, so the graph **curves upwards**.

Warming the thermistor gives more **electrons** enough **energy** to **escape** from their atoms. This means that there are **more charge carriers** available, so the **current increases** and the **resistance decreases** ($R = V/I$).

The **Resistance** of an **LDR** Depends on **Light Intensity**

LDR circuit symbol:

LDR stands for **Light-Dependent Resistor**. The **greater** the intensity of **light** shining on an LDR, the **lower** its **resistance**.

The explanation for this is similar to that for the thermistor. In this case, **light** provides the **energy** that releases more electrons. This means more charge carriers, which means a higher current and a lower resistance.

Diodes Only Let **Current Flow** in **One Direction**

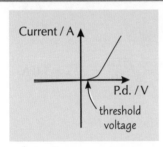

Diodes (including light-emitting diodes (LEDs)) are designed to let **current flow** in **one direction** only. You don't need to be able to explain how they work, just what they do.

1) **Forward bias** is the **direction** in which the **current** is **allowed to flow** — it's the direction the triangle points in the circuit symbols on the right.

2) **Most** diodes require a **threshold voltage** of about **0.6 V** in the **forward direction** before they will conduct.

3) In **reverse bias**, the **resistance** of the diode is **very high** and the current that flows is **very tiny**.

Diode circuit symbol:

LED circuit symbol:

Practice Questions

Q1 If an *I-V* graph is a straight line through the origin, what does this tell you about the resistance?

Q2 Draw an *I-V* characteristic graph for a resistor.

Q3 What is an LDR?

Q4 Draw an *I-V* characteristic graph for a diode. Label the areas of forward bias and reverse bias.

Exam Question

Q1 a) Sketch a characteristic *I-V* graph for a filament lamp. [1 mark]

b) Explain how increasing the voltage across a filament lamp affects its resistance, with reference to the mean drift velocity of electrons in the lamp. [4 marks]

c) Explain how the resistance of an NTC thermistor changes with temperature. [3 marks]

You light up my world like an LED — with One-Directional current...

Make sure you learn all these graphs and can explain them all. It's all about energy — for metals, more energy means more heat and a higher resistance. For semiconductors, more energy means more charge carriers and lower resistance.

Electrical Energy and Power

Power and energy are pretty familiar concepts — and here they are again. Same principles, just different equations.

Power is the Rate of Transfer of Energy

Power (P) is **defined** as the **rate** of **doing work**. It's measured in **watts (W)**, where **1 watt** is equivalent to **1 joule of work done per second**.

in symbols: $\boxed{P = \dfrac{W}{t}}$

There's a really simple formula for **power** in **electrical circuits**:

$$\boxed{P = VI}$$

In an electrical circuit, W is the work done moving a charge.

This makes sense, since:

1) **Potential difference (V)** is defined as the **work done** per **coulomb**.
2) **Current (I)** is defined as the **number** of **coulombs** transferred per **second**.
3) So **p.d.** × **current** is **work done per second**, i.e. **power**.

You also know (from the definition of **resistance**) that $V = IR$ (see p.44).
Combining this with the equation above gives you loads of **different ways** to **calculate power**.

$$P = VI \qquad\qquad P = \frac{V^2}{R} \qquad\qquad P = I^2R$$

Obviously, which equation you should use depends on what **quantities** you're given in the **question**.

Arnold had a pretty high resistance to doing work.

Example: A robotic mutant Santa from the future converts 750 J of electrical energy into heat every second.
a) What is the operating power of the robotic mutant Santa?
b) All of the robotic mutant Santa's components are connected in series, with a total resistance of 30 Ω. What current flows through his wire veins?

a) Power $= W \div t = 750 \div 1 = \textbf{750 W}$
b) $P = I^2R$ so $I = \sqrt{\dfrac{P}{R}} = \sqrt{\dfrac{750}{30}} = \sqrt{25} = \textbf{5.0 A}$

Energy is Easy to Calculate if you Know the Power

Sometimes it's the **total energy** transferred that you're interested in. In this case you simply need to **multiply** the **power** by the **time**. So: $\boxed{W = VIt}$ (or $W = \dfrac{V^2}{R}t$ or $W = I^2Rt$)

Make sure that the time is in seconds before you use these equations.

Example: The circuit diagram on the right is part of an electric kettle. A current of 4.0 A flows through the kettle's heating element once it is connected to the mains (230 V).
The kettle takes 4.5 minutes to boil the water it contains. How much energy does the kettle's heating element transfer to the water in the time it takes to boil?

230 V

kettle heating element

Time the kettle takes to boil in seconds $= 4.5 \times 60 = 270$ seconds.
Use the equation $W = VIt = 230 \times 4.0 \times 270 = 248\,400$ J $= \textbf{250 kJ (to 2 s.f.)}$

Remember, this is the circuit symbol for an open switch:

This is a closed switch:

Electrical Energy and Power

You can **Investigate** the **Power Output** of an **Electric Motor**

1) Attach a mass, **m**, to a motor, as shown on the right, and connect the motor to the **circuit** shown. When you close the switch, the motor will **turn on**, winding the string around the axle and **raising the mass**.

2) Record the **time taken**, **t**, for the motor to raise the mass a **set distance**, Δh, e.g. 50 cm, using a **stopwatch** and the metre ruler.

3) Calculate the **work done against gravity** by the motor to raise the mass using the equation: $\Delta E_{grav} = mg\Delta h$ (see p.36).

4) You can then calculate the **power output** of the motor, using the equation $P = W/t$ (p.48).

5) You could also investigate the **efficiency** of the motor when lifting a given mass using this equipment. You'd need to measure the **potential difference** across the motor, and the **current** through it, as it lifts the load (see the circuit diagram on the right). You could then calculate the input power using $P = VI$.

6) You could then calculate the efficiency of the motor using the equation: **Efficiency = (useful power output ÷ total power input)** (see page 37). The motor won't be **100% efficient** as some energy will be lost, e.g. as heat to **resistance** in the circuit components.

7) You could also use this apparatus to investigate whether the power input and power output of the motor **varies** with the **load** attached to it by **varying the mass** attached to it.

(Voltmeter and ammeter only required for efficiency experiment.)

Practice Questions

Q1 Power is measured in watts. What is 1 watt equivalent to?

Q2 What equation links power, voltage and resistance?

Q3 Write down the equation linking power, current and resistance.

Q4 Describe how you could investigate the power output of an electric motor when raising different loads.

Exam Questions

Q1 The circuit diagram for a mains-powered hairdryer is shown below.

a) The heater has a power of 920 W in normal operation. Calculate the current in the heater. [1 mark]

b) The motor's resistance is 190 Ω. Calculate the current through the motor when the hairdryer is used. [1 mark]

c) Show that the total power of the hairdryer in normal operation is just under 1.2 kW. [2 marks]

Q2 A 12 V car battery supplies a current of 48 A for 2.0 seconds to the car's starter motor. The total resistance of the connecting wires is 0.010 Ω.

a) Calculate the energy transferred by the battery in this time. [1 mark]

b) Calculate the energy wasted as heat in the wires. [1 mark]

Ultimate cosmic powers...

Another load of equations on these pages to add to your collection, oh joy. Make sure you learn the circuit symbol for a heater in exam question 1 — you won't get a key in the exam (I gave you one because I'm nice).

E.m.f and Internal Resistance

There's resistance everywhere — inside batteries, in all the wires (although it's very small) and in the circuit components themselves. Who said current had it easy?

Batteries have an **Internal Resistance**

Resistance in metals comes from **electrons colliding** with **atoms** (or ions) and **losing energy** (see p.46).

In a **battery**, **chemical energy** is used to make **electrons move**. As they move, they collide with atoms inside the battery — so batteries **must** have resistance. This is called **internal resistance**.

Internal resistance is what makes **batteries** and **cells warm up** when they're used.

Chemical reactions in the battery produce electrical energy.

Internal resistance (**r**)

Because the resistance of wires is so small, on these two pages I'm assuming they have zero resistance.

In general, r is typically less than 1 ohm for a battery. This means a high current can flow.

Load resistance (**R**)

Load resistance is the total resistance of all the components in the external circuit. You might see it called 'external resistance'.

1) The total amount of **work** the battery does on each **coulomb** of charge is called its **electromotive force** or **e.m.f.** (ε). Be careful — e.m.f. **isn't** actually a force. It's measured in **volts**.

$$W = \varepsilon Q \quad \text{or} \quad \varepsilon = \frac{W}{Q}$$

W is the work done on the charge (i.e. the energy transferred to the charge) in joules.

2) The **potential difference** across the **load resistance** (**R**) is the **work done** when **one coulomb** of charge flows through the **load resistance**. This potential difference is called the **terminal p.d.** (**V**).

3) If there was **no internal resistance**, the **terminal p.d.** would be the **same** as the **e.m.f.** However, in **real** power supplies, there's **always some energy lost** overcoming the internal resistance.

4) The **energy wasted per coulomb** overcoming the internal resistance is called the **lost volts** (**v**).

Conservation of energy tells us:

| energy per coulomb supplied by the source | = | energy per coulomb used in load resistance | + | energy per coulomb wasted in internal resistance |

There are Loads of **Calculations** with **E.m.f.** and **Internal Resistance**

Examiners can ask you to do **calculations** with **e.m.f.** and **internal resistance** in loads of **different** ways. You've got to be ready for whatever they throw at you.

$$\varepsilon = V + v \qquad \varepsilon = I(R + r) \qquad V = \varepsilon - v \qquad \varepsilon = V + Ir$$

These are all basically the **same equation**, just written differently. If you're given enough information you can calculate the e.m.f. (ε), terminal p.d. (**V**), lost volts (**v**), current (**I**), load resistance (**R**) or internal resistance (**r**). Which equation you should use depends on what information you've got, and what you need to calculate.

You Can Work Out the **E.m.f.** of **Multiple** Cells in **Series** or **Parallel**

For cells **in series**, you can calculate the **total e.m.f.** of the cells by **adding** their individual e.m.f.s.

$$\varepsilon_{total} = \varepsilon_1 + \varepsilon_2 + \varepsilon_3 + \ldots$$

This makes sense if you think about it, because each charge goes through each of the cells and so gains e.m.f. from each one.

For identical cells **in parallel**, the **total e.m.f.** of the combination of cells is the **same size** as the e.m.f. of each of the individual cells.

See p.52 for all the rules for parallel and series circuits.

$$\varepsilon_{total} = \varepsilon_1 = \varepsilon_2 = \varepsilon_3 = \ldots$$

This is because the current will split equally between identical cells. The charge only gains e.m.f. from the cells it travels through — so the overall e.m.f. in the circuit doesn't increase.

E.m.f and Internal Resistance

Time for an Example E.m.f. Calculation Question...

Example Three identical cells each with an e.m.f. of 2.0 V and an internal resistance of 0.20 Ω are connected in parallel in the circuit shown to the right. A current of 0.90 A is flowing through the circuit. Calculate the total p.d. across the cells.

First calculate the lost volts, v, for 1 cell using $v = Ir$.

Since the current flowing through the circuit is split equally between each of the three cells, the current through one cell is $I/3$. So for 1 cell: $v = I/3 \times r = 0.90/3 \times 0.20 = 0.30 \times 0.20 = 0.06$ V

Then find the terminal p.d. across 1 cell using the equation: $V = \varepsilon - v = 2 - 0.06 = 1.94$ V

So the total p.d. across the cells combined = **1.9 V (to 2 s.f.)**

Investigate Internal Resistance and E.m.f. With This Circuit

1) **Vary** the **current** in the circuit by changing the value of the **load resistance** (R) using the variable resistor. **Measure** the p.d. (V) for several different values of **current** (I).

2) Record your data for V and I in a table, and **plot the results** in a graph of V against I.

To find the **e.m.f.** and **internal resistance** of the cell, start with the equation: $\boxed{\varepsilon = V + Ir}$

1) Rearrange to give $V = -rI + \varepsilon$

2) Since ε and r are constants, that's just the equation of a **straight line**:

Equation of a straight line
$$y = mx + c$$
gradient   y-intercept

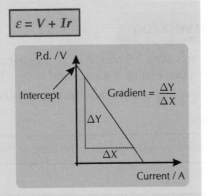

P.d. /V

Intercept   Gradient = $\frac{\Delta Y}{\Delta X}$

ΔY

ΔX

Current / A

3) So the intercept on the vertical axis is ε.

4) And the gradient is $-r$.

You probably don't need to take repeated readings in an experiment like this one, but make sure you get plenty of data points to draw your line.

An **easier** way to **measure** the **e.m.f.** of a **power source** to just connect a **voltmeter** across its **terminals**. Voltmeters have a very **high resistance**, but a **small current** will still flow through them. This means there must be some **lost volts**, which means you measure a value **very slightly less** than the **e.m.f.** (Although in practice the difference isn't usually significant.)

Practice Questions

Q1 What causes internal resistance? Write down the equation linking work, e.m.f. and charge.

Q2 What is the difference between e.m.f. and terminal p.d.?

Q3 What is meant by 'lost volts'?

Q4 Give an example of a source of e.m.f and describe an experiment to find the value of its e.m.f.

Exam Questions

Q1 A battery with an internal resistance of 0.8 Ω and an e.m.f. of 24 V powers a dentist's drill with resistance 4.0 Ω.

a) Calculate the current in the circuit when the drill is connected to the power supply. [1 mark]

b) Calculate the voltage across the drill while it is being used. [1 mark]

Q2 A bulb of resistance R is powered by two cells connected in series, each with internal resistance r and e.m.f. ε. Which expression represents the current flowing through each cell? [1 mark]

A $\frac{\varepsilon}{R+r}$ B $\frac{\varepsilon}{2(R+2r)}$ C $\frac{2\varepsilon}{R+2r}$ D $\frac{\varepsilon}{R+2r}$

Why'd the physicist swallow a multimeter? To find his internal resistance...

Thank you, thank you, I'm here all week. A jam-packed pair of pages here, but it's all stuff you need to know. Make sure you know the difference between terminal p.d. and e.m.f., and that you've got a handle on all those equations.

Conservation of Charge & Energy in Circuits

There are some things in Physics that are so fundamental that you just have to accept them. Like the fact that there's loads of Maths in it. And that energy is conserved. And that Physicists get more homework than everyone else.

Charge Doesn't 'Leak Away' Anywhere — it's Conserved

1) As **charge flows** through a circuit, it **doesn't** get **used up** or **lost**.

2) This means that whatever charge flows **into** a junction will flow **out** again.

3) Since **current** is **rate of flow of charge**, it follows that whatever current flows **into** a junction is the same as the current flowing **out** of it.

Example: 6 coulombs of charge flow into a junction in 1 second, and split in the ratio 1:2.

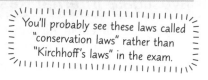

$Q_1 = 6\,C \Rightarrow I_1 = 6\,A$

at junction, current branches in two

$Q_2 = 2\,C \Rightarrow I_2 = 2\,A$

$Q_3 = 4\,C \Rightarrow I_3 = 4\,A$

$I_1 = I_2 + I_3$

Kirchhoff's first law says:

> The total **current entering a junction** = the total **current leaving it**.

You'll probably see these laws called "conservation laws" rather than "Kirchhoff's laws" in the exam.

Energy is Conserved too

1) **Energy is conserved.** You already know that. In **electrical circuits**, **energy** is **transferred round** the circuit. Energy **transferred to** a unit charge is **e.m.f.**, and energy **transferred from** a unit charge is **potential difference**.

2) In a **closed loop**, these two quantities must be **equal** if energy is conserved (which it is).

Kirchhoff's second law says:

> The **total e.m.f.** around a **series circuit** = the **sum** of the **p.d.s** across each component.

(or $\varepsilon = \Sigma IR$ in symbols)

The Conservation Laws Apply to Different Combinations of Resistors

A **typical exam question** will give you a **circuit** with bits of information missing, leaving you to fill in the gaps. Not the most fun... but on the plus side you get to ignore any internal resistance stuff (unless the question tells you otherwise)... hurrah. You need to remember the **following rules:**

Series Circuits:

1) **same current at all points** of the circuit (since there are no junctions)

2) **e.m.f. split between components** (by Kirchhoff's 2nd law), so:
$\varepsilon = V_1 + V_2 + V_3$

3) $V = IR$, so if I is constant:
$IR_{total} = IR_1 + IR_2 + IR_3$

4) cancelling the Is gives:

$$R_{total} = R_1 + R_2 + R_3$$

Parallel Circuits:

1) **current is split at each junction**, so: $I = I_1 + I_2 + I_3$

2) **same p.d. across all components** (remember that within a loop the e.m.f. equals the sum of individual p.d.s)

3) so, $V/R_{total} = V/R_1 + V/R_2 + V/R_3$

4) cancelling the Vs gives:

$$\frac{1}{R_{total}} = \frac{1}{R_1} + \frac{1}{R_2} + \frac{1}{R_3}$$

...and there's an example on the next page to make sure you know what to do with all that...

Conservation of Charge & Energy in Circuits

Example:

A battery with an e.m.f. of 16 V and negligible internal resistance is connected in a circuit as shown on the right. The resistances are all correct to 2 s.f..

a) Show that the group of resistors between X and Y could be replaced by a single resistor of resistance 15 Ω.

You can find the combined resistance of the 15 Ω, 20 Ω and 12 Ω resistors using:

$1/R = 1/R_1 + 1/R_2 + 1/R_3 = 1/15 + 1/20 + 1/12 = 1/5 \Rightarrow R = 5 \Omega$

So overall resistance between X and Y can be found by: $R = R_1 + R_2 = 5 + 10 = \mathbf{15\ \Omega}$

b) If $R_A = 20 \Omega$ (to 2 s.f.):
   i) calculate the potential difference across R_A,

Careful — there are a few steps here. You need the p.d. across R_A, but you don't know the current through it. So start there: total resistance in circuit = 20 + 15 = 35 Ω, so current through R_A can be found using $I = V_{total}/R_{total} = 16/35$ A then you can use $V = IR_A$ to find the p.d. across R_A: $V = 16/35 \times 20 = \mathbf{9.1\ V}$ **(to 2 s.f.)**

   ii) calculate the current in the 15 Ω resistor.

You know the current flowing into the group of three resistors and out of it, but not through the individual branches. But you know that their combined resistance is 5 Ω from part a), so you can work out the p.d. across the group:

$V = IR = 16/35 \times 5 = 16/7$ V

The p.d. across the whole group is the same as the p.d. across each individual resistor, so you can use this to find the current through the 15 Ω resistor:

$I = V/R = (16/7) / 15 = \mathbf{0.15\ A}$ **(to 2 s.f.)**

Q1 State Kirchhoff's first and second laws and state what quantity is conserved in each case.

Q2 Show how conservation of charge leads to the rule for combining resistors in series: $R_{total} = R_1 + R_2 + R_3$.

Q3 Show how conservation of energy leads to the rule for combining resistors in parallel: $\frac{1}{R_{total}} = \frac{1}{R_1} + \frac{1}{R_2} + \frac{1}{R_3}$.

Q4 Find the current through and potential difference across each of two 5 Ω resistors when they are placed in a circuit containing a 5 V battery, and are wired: a) in series, b) in parallel.

Exam Question

Q1 For the circuit on the right:

a) Calculate the total effective resistance of the three resistors in this combination. [2 marks]

b) Calculate the main current, I_3. [1 mark]

c) Calculate the potential difference across the 4.0 Ω resistor. [1 mark]

d) Calculate the potential difference across the parallel pair of resistors. [1 mark]

e) Calculate the currents I_1 and I_2. [2 marks]

Conservation of energy is really important — time for a nap I think...

V = IR is the formula you'll use most often in these questions. Make sure you know whether you're using it on the overall circuit, or just one specific component. It's amazingly easy to get muddled up — you've been warned.

The Potential Divider

*I remember the days when potential dividers were pretty much the hardest thing they could throw at you.
Then along came A level Physics. Hey ho. Anyway, in context this doesn't seem too hard now, so get stuck in.*

Use a **Potential Divider** to get a **Fraction** of a **Source Voltage**

1) At its simplest, a **potential divider** is a circuit with a **voltage source** and a couple of **resistors** in series.

2) The **potential difference** across the voltage source (e.g. a battery) is **split** in the **ratio** of the **resistances** (p.52).

3) So, if you had a **2 Ω** resistor and a **3 Ω** resistor, you'd get **2/5** of the p.d. across the **2 Ω** resistor and **3/5** across the **3 Ω**.

4) You can use potential dividers to supply a potential difference, V_{out}, between **zero** and the potential difference across the voltage source. This can be useful, e.g. if you need a **varying** p.d. supply or one that is at a **lower p.d.** than the voltage source.

The voltage has **dropped** by V_1 (the voltage across R_1) by the time it gets to here. The **remaining voltage** that can be supplied, e.g. to another component, is V_{out}.

In the circuit shown, R_2 has $\frac{R_2}{R_1 + R_2}$ of the total resistance. So: $\boxed{V_{out} = \frac{R_2}{R_1 + R_2} V_s}$

E.g. if $V_s = 9$ V and you want V_{out} to be 6 V, then you need:

$$\frac{R_2}{R_1 + R_2} = \frac{2}{3} \text{ which gives } R_2 = 2R_1$$

So you could have, say, $R_1 = 100\ \Omega$, $R_2 = 200\ \Omega$

5) This circuit is mainly used for **calibrating voltmeters**, which have a **very high resistance**.

6) If you put something with a **relatively low resistance** across R_2 though, you start to run into **problems**. You've **effectively** got **two resistors** in **parallel**, which will **always** have a **total** resistance **less** than R_2. That means that V_{out} will be **less** than you've calculated, and will depend on what's connected across R_2. Hrrumph.

Use a **Variable Resistor** to Vary the **Voltage**

If you replace R_1 with a **variable resistor**, you can change V_{out}. When $R_1 = 0$, $V_{out} = V_s$. As you increase R_1, V_{out} gets smaller.

Add an **LDR** or **Thermistor** for a **Light** or **Temperature Sensor**

1) A **light-dependent resistor** (LDR) has a very **high resistance** in the **dark**, but a **lower resistance** in the **light**.

2) An **NTC thermistor** has a **high resistance** at **low temperatures**, but a much **lower resistance** at **high temperatures** (it varies in the opposite way to a normal resistor, only much more so).

3) Either of these can be used as one of the **resistors** in a **potential divider**, giving an **output voltage** that **varies** with the **light level** or **temperature**.

See page 47 for why the resistances of LDRs and NTC thermistors change like this.

The diagram shows a **sensor** used to detect **light levels**.

When light shines on the LDR its **resistance decreases**, so V_{out} increases.

You can include LDRs and thermistors in circuits that control **switches**, e.g. to turn on a light or a heating system.

If you replace the LDR with an NTC thermistor, V_{out} will increase with temperature.

The Potential Divider

A *Potentiometer* uses a *Variable Resistor* to give a *Variable Voltage*

1) Imagine you have a long length of wire connected to a power supply. If the wire is **uniform** (i.e. same cross-sectional area and material throughout), then its **resistance** is **proportional** to its **length**.

2) This means that if you were to connect a voltmeter across different lengths of the wire, the **potential difference** you'd record would be **proportional** to the **length** you'd connected it over — you're measuring across a bigger share of the total resistance so you get a bigger potential difference.

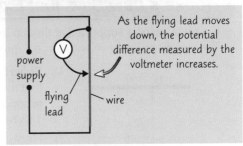

As the flying lead moves down, the potential difference measured by the voltmeter increases.

3) This is the basis of how a **potentiometer** works. A **potentiometer** is basically a potential divider, with a variable resistor replacing R_1 and R_2 (it's even sometimes **called** a potential divider just to confuse things).

4) You move a **slider** or turn a knob to **adjust** the **relative sizes** of R_1 and R_2. That way you can vary V_{out} from **0 V** up to the source voltage.

5) This is dead handy when you want to be able to **change** a **voltage continuously**, like in the **volume control** of a stereo:

Example:

Here, V_s is replaced by the input signal (e.g. from a CD player) and V_{out} is the output to the amplifier and loudspeaker.

I've often wished bagpipes had a volume control. Or just an off switch.

Practice Questions

Q1 Look at the light sensor circuit on page 54.
How could you change the circuit so that it could be used to detect temperature changes?

Q2 The LDR in the circuit on page 54 has a resistance of 300 Ω when in light conditions, and 900 Ω in dark conditions. The fixed resistor has a value of 100 Ω. Show that V_{out} (light) = 1.5 V and V_{out} (dark) = 0.6 V.

Exam Questions

Q1 In the circuit on the right, all the resistors have the same value. Calculate the p.d. between:

a) A and B. [1 mark]

b) A and C. [1 mark]

c) B and C. [1 mark]

12 V

Q2 Look at the circuit on the right. All the resistances are given to 2 significant figures.

a) Calculate the p.d. between A and B as shown by a high resistance voltmeter placed between the two points. [1 mark]

b) A 40.0 Ω resistor is now placed between points A and B. Calculate the p.d. across AB and the current flowing through the 40.0 Ω resistor. [4 marks]

OI... YOU... [bang bang bang]... turn that potentiometer down...

You'll probably have to use a potentiometer in every experiment you do with electricity from now on in, so you'd better get used to them. I can't stand the things myself, but then lab and me don't mix — far too technical.

Hooke's Law

Hooke's law applies to all materials, but only up to a point. For some materials that point is so tiny you wouldn't notice...

Hooke's Law Says that Extension is Proportional to Force

If a **metal wire** is supported at the top and then a weight attached to the bottom, it **stretches**.
The weight pulls down with force **F**, producing an equal and opposite force at the support.

The material will only deform (stretch, bend, twist etc.) if there's a pair of opposite forces acting on it.

1) **Robert Hooke** discovered in the 17th century that the extension of a stretched wire, Δx, is proportional to the change in load or force, ΔF. This relationship is now called **Hooke's law**.

2) Hooke's law can be written:

$$\Delta F = k\Delta x$$

Where **k** is the stiffness of the object that is being stretched. **k** is called the **force constant** (or **stiffness constant**) and has units Nm^{-1}.

Hooke's Law Also Applies to Springs

A metal spring also changes length when you apply a **pair of opposite forces**.

1) The **extension** or **compression** of a spring is **proportional** to the **force** applied — so Hooke's law applies.

2) For springs, **k** in the formula $\Delta F = k\Delta x$ can also be called the **spring stiffness** or **spring constant**.

Hooke's law works just as well for **compressive** forces as **tensile** forces. For a spring, **k** has the **same value** whether the forces are tensile or compressive (that's not true for all materials).

3) **Hooke's Law** doesn't just apply to metal **springs** and **wires** — most **other materials** obey it up to a point.

Tensile forces create <u>tension</u> in a stretched spring. Compressive forces create compression in a squashed spring. Tensile or compressive forces in the spring act in the opposite direction to the tensile or compressive forces stretching or squashing it.

Hooke's Law Stops Working when the Load is Great Enough

There's a **limit** to the force you can apply for Hooke's law to stay true.

1) The graph shows force against extension for a **typical metal wire** or **spring**.

2) The first part of the graph (up to point P) shows Hooke's law being obeyed — there's a **straight-line relationship** between **force** and **extension**.

3) When the force becomes great enough, the graph starts to **curve**. **Metals** generally obey Hooke's law up to the **limit of proportionality**, **P**.

4) The point marked **E** on the graph is called the **elastic limit**. If you exceed the elastic limit, the material will be **permanently stretched**. When all the force is removed, the material will be **longer** than at the start.

5) Be careful — there are some materials, like **rubber**, that only obey Hooke's law for **really small** extensions.

A Deformation can be Elastic or Plastic

A material will show elastic deformation **up to** its **elastic limit**, and plastic deformation **beyond** it.
If a **deformation** is **elastic**, the material returns to its **original shape** once the forces are removed.

1) When the material is put under **tension**, the **atoms** of the material are **pulled apart** from one another.

2) Atoms can **move** slightly relative to their **equilibrium positions**, without changing position in the material.

3) Once the **load** is **removed**, the atoms **return** to their **equilibrium** distance apart.

If a deformation is **plastic**, the material is **permanently stretched**.

1) Some atoms in the material move position relative to one another.

2) When the load is removed, the **atoms don't return** to their original positions.

Extension and compression are sometimes called <u>tensile deformation</u> and <u>compressive deformation</u>.

Hooke's Law

Investigating Extension

1) Set up the experiment shown in the diagram. Support the object being tested at the top (e.g. with a clamp) and measure its original (natural) length with a ruler.

2) Add weights one at a time to the bottom of the object.

3) After each weight is added, measure the new length of the object, then **calculate the extension**:

> **extension = new length – original length**

4) To measure an extension as **accurately** as possible, make sure you fix a ruler close to the extending object and take readings with your eye close to the ruler. It's a good idea to use a '**fiducial marker**' (a thin tag on the object that marks where you're measuring) and a set square to ensure the ruler is vertical. Make sure the marker and ruler are both at eye level when you take readings.

5) Plot a graph of **force** (weight) against **extension** for your results. Where the line of best fit is **straight**, then the object obeys Hooke's law and the gradient = **k** (as $\Delta F = k\Delta x$). If you've loaded the object beyond its limit of proportionality, the graph will start to curve.

6) Make sure you carry out the experiment **safely**. You should be **standing up** so you can get out of the way quickly if the weights fall, and wearing **safety goggles** to protect your eyes in case the object snaps.

Object being tested — Clamp and clamp stand — Weights — Ruler

Example: A student investigates extension using the set-up shown above, and plots their results on the graph below. Find the stiffness of the object being stretched.

The stiffness of the object, k, is the gradient of the graph up to the limit of proportionality.

For this graph, this is shortly after the point where the load is 3.0 N and the extension is 2.0 mm.

Convert 2.0 mm into m, to get 0.0020 m.

Then $k = \dfrac{\Delta F}{\Delta x} = \dfrac{3.0}{0.0020} = $ **1500 Nm^{-1}**.

If the markings on your measuring equipment are quite far apart, you can often interpolate between them (e.g. if the length is halfway between the markings for 24 mm and 25 mm you could record it as 24.5 mm). But it's better to use something with a finer scale if you can.

Practice Questions

Q1 State Hooke's law and explain what is meant by the elastic limit of a material.

Q2 Define tensile forces and compressive forces.

Q3 From studying the force-extension graph for a material as it is loaded and unloaded, how can you tell:
   a) if Hooke's law is being obeyed,   b) if the elastic limit has been reached?

Q4 What is meant by plastic deformation of a material?

Q5 Describe how you could determine the stiffness of an object being stretched, k, experimentally.

Exam Questions

Q1 A metal guitar string stretches 4.0 mm when a 10.0 N force is applied.

   a) If the string obeys Hooke's law, calculate how far the string will stretch when a 15 N force is applied. [1 mark]

   b) Calculate the force constant for this string in Nm^{-1}. [1 mark]

   c) The string is then stretched beyond its elastic limit. Describe the effect this will have on the string. [1 mark]

Q2 A rubber band is 6.0 cm long. When it is loaded with 2.5 N, its length becomes 10.4 cm. Further loading increases the length to 16.2 cm when the force is 5.0 N.

   State whether the rubber band obeys Hooke's law when the force on it is 5.0 N. Explain your answer. [2 marks]

Sod's Law — if you don't learn it, it'll be in the exam...

Three things you didn't know about Robert Hooke — he was the first person to use the word 'cell' (as in biology, not prisons), he helped Christopher Wren with his designs for St. Paul's Cathedral and no-one's sure what he looked like. I'd like to think that if I did all that stuff, then someone would at least remember what I looked like — poor old Hooke.

Stress, Strain and Elastic Strain Energy

How much a material stretches for a particular applied force depends on its dimensions. If you want to compare it to another material, you need to use stress and strain instead. A stress-strain graph is the same for any sample of a particular material — the size of the sample doesn't matter.

A Stress Causes a Strain

A material subjected to a pair of **opposite forces** might **deform** (i.e. **change shape**).
If the forces **stretch** the material, they're **tensile**. If the forces **squash** the material, they're **compressive**.

1) **Tensile stress**, σ, is defined as the **force applied**, F, divided by the **cross-sectional area**, A:

$$\sigma = \frac{F}{A}$$

The **units** of stress are **Nm⁻²** or pascals, **Pa**.

2) **Tensile strain**, ε, is defined as the **change in length** (i.e. the **extension**), divided by the **original length** of the material:

$$\varepsilon = \frac{\Delta x}{x}$$

Strain has **no units**, it's just a **ratio** and is usually written as a **number**. It can also be written as a **percentage**, e.g. extending a 0.5 m wire by 0.02 m would produce a strain of $(0.02 \div 0.5) \times 100 = 4\%$.

3) It doesn't matter whether the forces producing the **stress** and **strain** are **tensile** or **compressive** — the **same equations** apply. The only difference is that you tend to think of **tensile** forces as **positive**, and **compressive** forces as **negative**.

A Stress Big Enough to Break the Material is Called the Breaking Stress

As a greater and greater tensile **force** is applied to a material, the **stress** on it **increases**.

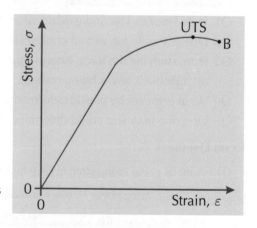

1) The effect of the **stress** is to start to **pull** the **atoms apart** from one another.

2) Eventually the stress becomes **so great** that atoms **separate completely**, and the **material breaks**. This is shown by point **B** on the graph. The stress at which this occurs is called the **breaking stress**.

3) The point marked **UTS** on the graph is called the **ultimate tensile stress**. This is the **maximum stress** that the material can withstand.

4) Both **UTS** and **B** depend on conditions e.g. **temperature**.

5) **Engineers** have to consider the **UTS** and **breaking stress** of materials when designing a **structure** — e.g. they need to make sure the stress on a material won't reach the **UTS** when the **conditions change**.

Elastic Strain Energy is the Area under a Force-Extension Graph

1) **Work** has to be done to **stretch** a material.

2) **Before** the **elastic limit** is reached, **all** this **work done** in stretching is **stored** as **elastic strain energy** in the material.

3) On a **graph** of **force against extension**, the elastic strain energy is given by the **area under the graph**.

4) If the force-extension graph is **non-linear**, you'll need to **estimate** the area by **counting squares** or dividing the curve into **trapeziums** (see page 25).

Stress, Strain and Elastic Strain Energy

Provided a material obeys Hooke's law, the **potential energy** stored inside it can be **calculated** quite easily.

1) The work done on the material in stretching it is equal to the energy stored.

2) **Work done** equals **force × displacement**.

3) However, the **force** on the material **isn't constant**. It rises from zero up to force F.
   To calculate the **work done**, use the **average force** between zero and F, i.e. $\frac{1}{2}F$: $\Longrightarrow$ $\boxed{\textbf{work done} = \frac{1}{2}F\Delta x}$

4) So the **elastic strain energy** stored, E_{el}, is: $\boxed{\Delta E_{el} = \frac{1}{2}F\Delta x}$ $\longleftarrow$ This is the triangular area under the force-extension graph — see previous page.

5) Because Hooke's law is being obeyed, $\Delta F = k\Delta x$,
   which means F can be replaced in the equation to give: $\boxed{\Delta E_{el} = \frac{1}{2}k\Delta x^2}$

Example: A metal wire is 55.0 cm long. A force of 550 N is applied to the wire, and the wire stretches. The length of the stretched wire is 56.5 cm. Calculate the elastic strain energy stored in the wire.

The extension of the wire is $\Delta x = 56.5$ cm $- 55.0$ cm $= 1.5$ cm $= 0.015$ m

So the elastic strain energy $\Delta E_{el} = \frac{1}{2} \times F \times \Delta x$
$= \frac{1}{2} \times 550 \times 0.015 = 4.125$ J $= \textbf{4.1 J (to 2 s.f.)}$

Practice Questions

Q1 Write a definition for tensile stress.

Q2 Explain what is meant by the tensile strain on a material.

Q3 What is meant by the breaking stress of a material?

Q4 How can the elastic strain energy in a material under load be found from its force-extension graph?

Q5 The work done is usually calculated as force multiplied by displacement.
   Explain why the work done in stretching a wire is $\frac{1}{2}F\Delta x$.

Exam Questions

Q1 A steel wire is 2.00 m long. When a 300 N (to 3 s.f.) force is applied to the wire, it stretches by 4.0 mm.
   The wire has a circular cross-section with a diameter of 1.0 mm.
   a) Calculate the tensile stress in the wire. [2 marks]
   b) Calculate the tensile strain of the wire. [1 mark]

Q2 A copper wire (which obeys Hooke's law) is stretched by 3.0 mm when a force of 50.0 N is applied.
   a) Calculate the stiffness constant for this wire in Nm^{-1}. [2 marks]
   b) Calculate the value of the elastic strain energy in the stretched wire. [1 mark]

Q3 A force is applied to stretch an unknown material.
   The graph shows the force-extension graph for this stretch.
   Estimate the elastic strain energy stored in the material as a
   result of this stretch.

[2 marks]

Q4 A pinball machine contains a spring which is used to fire a small, light metal ball to start the game.
   The spring has a stiffness constant of 40.8 Nm^{-1}. It is compressed by 5.00 cm and then released to fire the ball.
   Calculate the maximum possible kinetic energy of the ball. [3 marks]

UTS a laugh a minute, this stuff...

...or it would be, if there were more jokes. But you know what they say — a stress causes a strain, and nobody likes strained jokes. So you'd better just get on with learning this stuff proper good like. And before you ask, no — grabbing a slingshot and shooting the neighbours' begonias doesn't count as 'revising the energy stored in a stretched material'.

The Young Modulus

Busy chap, Thomas Young. He did this work on tensile stress as something of a sideline. Light was his main thing.
He proved that light behaved like a wave, explained how we see in colour and worked out what causes astigmatism.

The **Young Modulus** is Stress ÷ Strain

When you apply a **load** to stretch a material, it experiences a **tensile stress** and a **tensile strain**.

1) Up to the **limit of proportionality** (see p.56), the stress and strain of a material are proportional to each other.

2) So below this limit, for a particular material, stress divided by strain is a **constant**. This constant is called the **Young modulus**, *E*.

$$\text{Young modulus} = E = \frac{\text{stress}}{\text{strain}} = \frac{\sigma}{\varepsilon}$$

Where σ = stress and ε = strain

> Remember that $\sigma = \frac{F}{A}$
> and $\varepsilon = \frac{\Delta x}{x}$ —
> see p.58 for more.

3) The **units** of the Young modulus are the same as stress (**Nm⁻²** or pascals), since strain has no units.

4) The Young modulus is a measure of the **stiffness** of a material.
It is used by **engineers** to make sure the materials they are using can withstand sufficient forces.

To **Find** the Young Modulus, You need a **Very Long Wire**

This is the experiment you're most likely to do in class:

wire fixed at one end — test wire — marker on wire — pulley — bench — ruler with mm markings — weights

"Okay, found one.
Now what?"

> Mum moment: if you're doing this experiment, wear safety goggles — if the wire snaps, it could get very messy...

1) The test wire should be thin, and as long as possible.
The **longer and thinner** the wire, the more it **extends** for the same force — this reduces the percentage uncertainty in your measurements.

2) First you need to find the **cross-sectional area** of the wire. Use a **micrometer** to measure the **diameter** of the wire in several places and take an **average** of your measurements. By assuming that the cross-section is **circular**, you can use the formula for the area of a circle:

$$\text{area of a circle} = \pi r^2$$

> The thickness of wires is sometimes given in swg (standard wire gauge) — a 36 swg wire has a radius of about 0.1 mm.

3) **Clamp** the wire to the bench (as shown in the diagram above) so you can hang **weights** off one end of it. Start with the **smallest weight** necessary to **straighten** the wire. (**Don't** include this weight in your final calculations.)

4) Measure the **distance** between the **fixed end of the wire** and the **marker** — this is your unstretched length.

5) Then if you increase the weight, the **wire stretches** and the **marker moves**.

> To reduce random errors you should use a thin marker on the wire, and always look from directly above the marker and ruler when measuring the extension.

6) **Increase** the **weight** in equal steps (e.g. 100 g intervals), recording the marker reading each time — the **extension** is the **difference** between this reading and the **unstretched length**. Because you can't take repeat readings (the wire might snap or be permanently stretched), you should take more readings than usual.

7) You can use your results from this experiment to calculate the **stress** and **strain** of the wire and plot a stress-strain curve (see next page).

(The other standard way of measuring the Young modulus in the lab is using **Searle's apparatus**. This is a bit more accurate, but it's harder to do and the equipment's more complicated.)

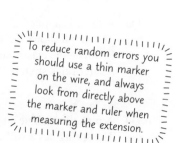

The Young Modulus

Use a *Stress-Strain Graph* to Find *E*

You can plot a **graph** of **stress against strain** from your results.

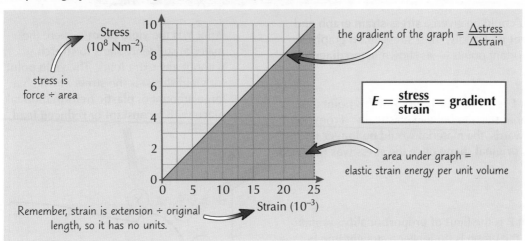

Stress (10⁸ Nm⁻²)

stress is force ÷ area

the gradient of the graph = $\frac{\Delta stress}{\Delta strain}$

$$E = \frac{\text{stress}}{\text{strain}} = \text{gradient}$$

area under graph = elastic strain energy per unit volume

Remember, strain is extension ÷ original length, so it has no units.

Strain (10⁻³)

1) The **gradient** of the graph gives the Young modulus, *E*.

2) The **area under the graph** gives the **strain energy** (or energy stored) per unit volume, i.e. the energy stored per 1 m³ of wire.

3) The stress-strain graph is a **straight line** provided that Hooke's law is obeyed, so you can also calculate the energy per unit volume (Jm⁻³) as:

energy per unit vol = ½ × stress × strain

Example: The stress-strain graph above is for a thin metal wire. Find the Young modulus of the wire from the graph.

E = stress ÷ strain = gradient

The gradient of the graph = $\frac{\Delta stress}{\Delta strain} = \frac{10 \times 10^8}{25 \times 10^{-3}}$

$= \mathbf{4 \times 10^{10} \ Nm^{-2}}$

Practice Questions

Q1 Define the Young modulus for a material. What are the units for the Young modulus?

Q2 Describe an experiment to find the Young modulus of a test wire. Explain why a thin test wire should be used.

Q3 What is given by the area contained under a stress-strain graph?

Exam Questions

Q1 A steel wire is stretched elastically. For a load of 80.0 N, the wire extends by 3.6 mm.
The original length of the wire was 2.50 m and its average diameter is 0.60 mm.
Calculate the value of the Young modulus for steel. [4 marks]

Q2 Two wires, A and B, are stretched elastically under a load of 50.0 N. The original length and the extension of both wires under this load are the same. The Young modulus of wire A is found to be 7.0×10^{10} Nm⁻².
The cross-sectional area of wire B is half that of wire A. Calculate the Young modulus of wire B. [2 marks]

Q3 The Young modulus for copper is 1.3×10^{11} Nm⁻².

a) The stress on a copper wire is 2.6×10^8 Nm⁻². Calculate the strain on the wire. [2 marks]

b) The load applied to the copper wire is 100 N (to 3 s.f.). Calculate the cross-sectional area of the wire. [2 marks]

c) Calculate the strain energy per unit volume for this loaded wire. [2 marks]

Learn that experiment — it's important...

Getting back to the good Dr Young... As if ground-breaking work in light, the physics of vision and materials science wasn't enough, he was also a well-respected physician, a linguist and an Egyptologist. He was one of the first to try to decipher the Rosetta stone (he didn't get it right, but nobody's perfect). Makes you feel kind of inferior, doesn't it...

Stress-Strain and Force-Extension Graphs

I hope the stresses and strains of this section aren't getting to you too much.

There are **Three Important Points** on a **Stress-Strain Graph**

In the exam you could be given a **stress-strain graph** and asked to **interpret** it. Luckily, most stress-strain graphs share **three** important points — as shown in the **diagram**.

Point **E** is the **elastic limit** — at this point the material starts to behave **plastically**. From point E onwards, the material would **no longer** return to its **original shape** once the stress was removed.

Point **P** is the **limit of proportionality** — after this, the graph is no longer a straight line but starts to **bend**. At this point, the material **stops** obeying **Hooke's law**, but would still **return** to its **original shape** if the stress was removed.

Before point **P**, the graph is a **straight line** through the **origin**. This shows that the material is obeying Hooke's law (page 56). The **gradient** of the line is constant — it's the **Young modulus** (see pages 60-61).

Point **Y** is the **yield point** — here the material suddenly starts to **stretch** without any extra load. The **yield point** (or yield stress) is the **stress** at which a large amount of **plastic deformation** takes place with a **constant** or **reduced load**.

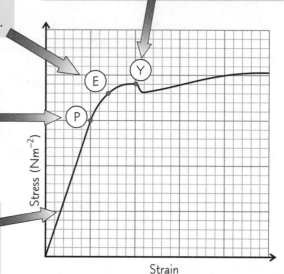

You might see the x-axis labelled as percentage strain instead — this is just the strain (a ratio) expressed as a percentage.

Stronger Materials can Withstand **More Stress** Before they **Break**

The graph below shows the stress-strain curves for materials of different strengths and stiffnesses.

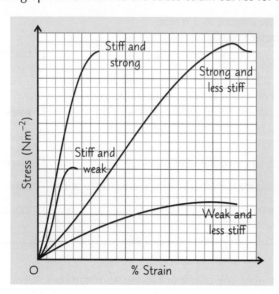

1) Different materials have different **breaking stresses** (p.58).
2) The **stronger** the material, the higher the breaking stress.
3) **Stiff** materials are difficult to stretch or compress. They have a **large** Young's modulus.
4) For a given stress, a stiff material will have a lower strain (i.e. a smaller extension) than a less stiff material.
5) A stiff material **doesn't** have to be strong (and vice versa). Some stiff materials **break** under a low stress, and some strong materials **aren't** very stiff.

When a line on a stress-strain graph just stops, you can assume the material has reached its breaking stress and fractured (unless the question says otherwise).

Steve took a break after a stressful day at the office.

Stress-Strain and Force-Extension Graphs

Force-Extension Graphs Are Similar to Stress-Strain Graphs

1) Force-extension graphs look a lot like **stress-strain** graphs, but they show slightly different things.
2) Force-extension graphs are **specific** for the tested **object** and **depend on its dimensions**. Stress-strain graphs describe the **general behaviour** of a **material**, they are **independent of the dimensions**.
3) You can plot a force-extension graph of what happens when you gradually **remove** a **force** from an object. The **unloading** line doesn't always match up with the **loading** line though.

You first met force-extension graphs on page 56.

A force-extension graph for a metal wire

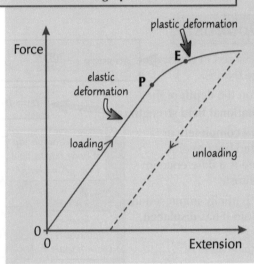

1) This graph is for a metal wire that has been stretched beyond its **limit of proportionality** (P) so the graph starts to **curve**.
2) When the load is **removed**, the **extension decreases**.
3) The unloading line is **parallel** to the loading line because the stiffness constant *k* is still the same (since the forces between the atoms are the same as they were during the loading).
4) But because the wire was stretched beyond its **elastic limit** (E) and deformed **plastically**, it has been **permanently stretched**. This means the unloading line doesn't go through the origin.
5) The **area** between the two lines is the **work done** to permanently deform the wire.

Of course, if you apply a big enough load to fracture the object, you can't draw an unloading line — you just get a force-extension graph like one of these graphs.

Practice Questions

Q1 What is the difference between the limit of proportionality and the elastic limit?
Q2 Describe what happens at the yield point.
Q3 A metal wire is stretched beyond its elastic limit. Why does the unloading line on the force-extension graph for the wire not go through the origin?

Exam Questions

Q1 Sketch a stress-strain graph to show (use the same axes):
a) A stiff and weak material being stretched to its breaking point. [1 mark]
b) A strong and less stiff material being stretched to its breaking point. [1 mark]

Q2 The diagram shows a stress-strain graph for a nylon thread.
a) State the yield stress for nylon. [1 mark]
b) Calculate how much energy per unit volume is stored in the thread when the limit of proportionality is reached. [2 marks]

I don't want to stress you, but this page can strain even the strongest brains...
The trick to revising is realising when you've really reached your yield point. That's when you need to take a break and get up and go for a walk. (It's not when you get the urge to have a quick check of your FaceTwittFeed or whatnot...)

Density, Upthrust and Viscosity

Yikes, three whole things in one go. Grab a coffee, take a deep breath and put on your snazziest learning hat...

Density is Mass per Unit Volume

Density is a measure of the '**compactness**' (for want of a better word) of a substance. It relates the **mass** of a substance to how much **space** it takes up.

1) The density of an object depends on what it's made of. Density **doesn't vary** with **size or shape**.

2) The **average density** of an object determines whether it **floats** or **sinks**. A solid object will **float** on a fluid if it has a **lower density** than the **fluid**.

> The symbol for density is a Greek letter rho (ρ) — it looks like a p but it isn't.

$$\text{density} = \frac{\text{mass}}{\text{volume}} \qquad \rho = \frac{m}{V}$$

The units of density are $g\,cm^{-3}$ or $kg\,m^{-3}$
$1\ g\,cm^{-3} = 1000\ kg\,m^{-3}$

Bodies in Fluids Experience Pressure and Upthrust

1) Pressure is the **amount of force** applied per **unit area**. It is measured in pascals **(Pa)**, which are equivalent to newtons per square metre (Nm^{-2}).

$$\text{pressure} = \frac{\text{force}}{\text{area}} \qquad p = \frac{F}{A}$$

2) The extra pressure acting on an object due to a fluid depends on the **depth** of the object in the fluid (h), the **density** of the fluid (ρ) and the **gravitational field strength** (g).

$$p = h\rho g$$

3) Upthrust is an **upward force** that fluids exert on objects that are **completely** or **partially submerged** in the fluid. It's caused because the top and bottom of a submerged object are at different depths. Since $p = h\rho g$, there is a difference in pressure which causes an overall upwards force known as upthrust.

4) **Archimedes' principle** says that when a body is completely or partially immersed in a fluid, it experiences an **upthrust** equal to the **weight** of the fluid it has **displaced**.

> **upthrust = weight of fluid displaced**

This is just because
$(h_2 - h_1)\rho g A = V\rho g = mg = W$

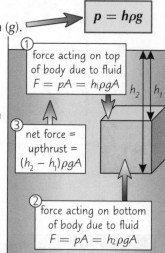

① force acting on top of body due to fluid $F = pA = h_1\rho g A$

③ net force = upthrust = $(h_2 - h_1)\rho g A$

② force acting on bottom of body due to fluid $F = pA = h_2\rho g A$

Example: Submarines make use of upthrust to dive underwater and return to the surface. To sink, large tanks are filled with water to **increase** the weight of the submarine so that it **exceeds** the upthrust. To rise to the surface, the tanks are filled with compressed air to **reduce** the weight so that it's **less** than the upthrust.

Viscous Drag Acts on Objects Moving Through Fluids

When an object moves through a fluid, or a fluid moves past an object, you get **friction** between the surface of the **object** and the **fluid**. This is **viscous drag**. You can calculate the **force due to viscous drag** on a **spherical** object moving through a fluid using **Stokes's law**.

$$F = 6\pi\eta r v$$

Viscous drag depends on the **viscosity** (or "thickness") of a fluid, η. Viscosity is **temperature-dependent** — **liquids** get **less viscous** as temperature **increases**, but **gases** (like **dry air**) get **more viscous** as temperature **increases**.

F is the viscous drag (N), η (eta) is the viscosity of the fluid (Nsm^{-2} or $Pa\,s$), r is the radius of the object (m) and v is the speed the object is moving at (ms^{-1}).

Stokes's Law Only Applies to Small Objects Moving Slowly with Laminar Flow

1) **Laminar flow** is a flow **pattern** where all the parts of the fluid are flowing in the **same direction** — the layers in the fluid **do not mix**.

2) Laminar flow usually occurs when a fluid is **flowing slowly**, or when an object is **moving slowly** through a fluid. The diagram shows a ball falling slowly with laminar flow.

3) **Turbulent flow** is a different flow **pattern**. You don't get nice layers like you do with laminar flow, all the parts of the **fluid** get **mixed up**.

4) Turbulent flow usually occurs when a **fluid** is flowing **quickly**, or an object is **moving quickly** through a fluid.

5) **Stokes's law only** applies to **small**, **spherical** objects moving **slowly** with **laminar flow**. It **doesn't** apply to **turbulent flow**.

Fluid 'layers'

What do you get if you cross a baby sheep with a river? A lamb in a flow.

Density, Upthrust and Viscosity

Measure the Viscosity of a Liquid

You can calculate the **viscosity** of a liquid by timing the **fall** of different sizes of ball bearings (little steel balls) of **known density**, ρ. using an experiment like this:

You don't have to use elastic bands — you could also use insulation tape or another marker for your intervals.

1) Fill a wide, clear tube with the liquid you want to investigate (e.g. washing up liquid). Make sure you know the **density** of the liquid, σ.

2) Put one rubber band about halfway down the tube at a position such that the ball bearings will have achieved **terminal velocity** (see page 30) when they reach it.

3) Place two more elastic bands **below** the first so that the distance between each band is **equal** and the lowest band is near the **bottom** of the tube. Record the distance between them. These are the points at which you will record t_1 and t_2.

4) Measure the diameter of your ball bearing and halve it to get the **radius**.

5) **Drop** the ball bearing into the tube. Start a **stopwatch** when the ball reaches the first band, and record the time at which it reaches each of the other bands. Record your results in a **table** (see below).

6) **Repeat** this at least three times for each ball bearing to reduce the effect of **random errors** on your results, then repeat the whole thing for different sizes of ball bearing. You can use a **strong magnet** to remove the ball bearings from the tube.

7) If the ball falls **close** to the **wall**, **re-do the reading** — the flow will no longer be laminar and Stokes's law will not apply.

8) **Calculate** the **average time taken** for each size of ball bearing to fall between the elastic bands. Use the **average time** and the **distance between bands** to calculate the **average (terminal) velocity** of the ball bearing between the elastic bands.

9) You can then calculate the **viscosity**, η, of the liquid. The ball bearings are falling at terminal velocity, so the **sum** of the forces acting on the ball is **zero**:

weight – drag – upthrust = 0

Substituting the equation for each force and rearranging gives $\eta = \dfrac{2r^2 g(\rho - \sigma)}{9v}$, where r is the radius of the ball bearing, g is the gravitational field strength due to gravity, ρ is the density of the ball bearing, σ is the density of the liquid and v is the average terminal velocity between the elastic bands.

10) Your table could look like this:

radius of ball bearing /mm	density of ball bearing / kg m^{-3}	time to t_1 / s	velocity at t_1 / ms^{-1}	time between t_1 and t_2 / s	velocity at t_2 / ms^{-1}	average velocity / ms^{-1}	viscosity / Nsm^{-2}	average viscosity / Nsm^{-2}
2.0		1		1				
		2		2				
		3		3				
3.0		1						
		2						

If the velocities at t_2 are consistently larger than those at t_1, the ball bearing might not have reached terminal velocity when you started timing — move the elastic bands down the tube a bit and try again.

Practice Questions

Q1 Show that the mass of 3.8 m³ of a liquid with density 1.5 kg m^{-3} is 5.7 kg.

Q2 State Archimedes's principle and explain how it is used by submarines.

Q3 What is meant by laminar flow?

Q4 Describe an experiment you could carry out to determine the viscosity of a liquid using ball bearings.

Exam Question

Q1 a) State Stokes's law and explain what each term represents. [1 mark]

b) State three conditions that must be true for Stokes's law to be apply. [3 marks]

c) A ball bearing of radius 3.0 mm is falling at a constant speed of 0.040 ms^{-1} through a liquid of viscosity 3.0 Pa s. The density of the liquid is 1400 kg m^{-3}. Calculate the weight of the ball bearing. ($V_{sphere} = \frac{4}{3}\pi r^3$) [5 marks]

My discosity increases with temperature — warm me up, I'll dance for hours...

Sorry about the 'lamb-in-a-flow' joke — it really is awful. My boss Joe thought it up, I'm just not that funny. If you're struggling to remember this page, try explaining it to someone else (little brothers are useful for this) — it really helps.

The Nature Of Waves

Aaaah... waggling ropes about. It's all good clean fun as my mate Richard used to say...

A **Wave** Transfers **Energy** Away From Its **Source**

A **progressive** (moving) wave carries **energy** from one place to another **without transferring any material**. The transfer of energy is in the **same direction** as the wave is **travelling**. Here are some ways you can tell waves carry energy:

1) Electromagnetic waves cause things to **heat up**.
2) **X-rays** and **gamma rays** knock electrons out of their orbits, causing **ionisation**.
3) Loud **sounds** cause large oscillations in air particles which can make things **vibrate**.
4) **Wave power** can be used to **generate electricity**.

Since waves carry energy away, the **source** of the wave **loses energy**.

You Need to Know These **Bits** of a **Wave**

1) **Displacement**, x, metres — how far a **point** on the wave has **moved** from its **undisturbed position**.
2) **Amplitude**, A, metres — the **maximum magnitude** of the **displacement**.
3) **Wavelength**, λ, metres — the **length** of **one whole wave cycle**, e.g. from **crest** to **crest** or **trough** to **trough**.

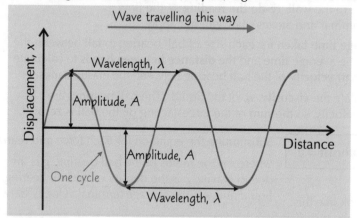

4) **Period**, T, seconds — the **time taken** for a **whole cycle** (vibration) to complete.
5) **Frequency**, f, hertz — the **number** of **cycles** (vibrations) **per second** passing a given **point**.
6) **Phase** — a measurement of the **position** of a certain **point** along the wave cycle.
7) **Phase difference** — the amount one wave lags behind another.

Phase and phase difference are measured in angles (in degrees or radians). See p.74.

The **Frequency** is the **Inverse** of the **Period**

$$\text{Frequency} = \frac{1}{\text{Period}}$$

$$f = \frac{1}{T}$$

It's that simple.
Get the **units** straight: **1 Hz = 1 s⁻¹**.

The **Wave Equation** Links **Wave Speed, Frequency** and **Wavelength**

1) **Wave speed** can be measured just like the speed of anything else:

$$\text{Wave speed } (v) = \frac{\text{Distance } (d)}{\text{Time } (t)}$$

2) You can use this equation to derive the **wave equation** (but thankfully you don't have to do that, you just need to be able to use it).

$$\text{Speed of wave } (v) = \text{frequency } (f) \times \text{wavelength } (\lambda)$$

$$v = f\lambda$$

Remember, you're not measuring how fast a physical point (like one molecule of rope) moves. You're measuring how fast a point on the **wave pattern** moves.

The Nature Of Waves

Oscilloscopes Display Waves

1) A cathode ray **oscilloscope** (CRO) measures **voltage**. It **displays** waves from a **signal generator** as a function of **voltage** over **time**.

2) The displayed wave is called a **trace**.

3) The screen is split into squares called **divisions**.

4) The vertical axis is in **volts**. The **volts per division** shown on this axis is controlled by the **gain dial**.

5) The horizontal axis is in **seconds** — also called the **timebase**. The **seconds per division** shown on this axis is controlled by the **timebase** dial.

6) You can alter the gain and timebase to make it **easy to read** off measurements.

Gain dial in volts/div

Screen split into divisions

Timebase dial in ms/div

The period of a wave is found from: the no. of divisions in one complete wave × the timebase setting.

If you plug an **AC (alternating current) supply** into an oscilloscope, you get a trace that goes up and down in a regular pattern — some of the time it's positive and some of the time it's negative. A **microphone** converts **sound waves** into **electrical signals** which can be seen on an **oscilloscope**.

An Oscilloscope Can be Used to Find the Speed of Sound

1) Set up the experiment as shown in the diagram below and set the **frequency** of the signal generator to around 2-6 kHz. A **2-beam oscilloscope** must be used as this can display **two waves** — one for the **signal generator** generating a **sound wave** and one for the **same sound wave** being **received** by the **microphone**.

2) A 2-beam oscilloscope has **three dials** — two are the gain dials for **each** input signal and the other dial is the timebase dial for **both** input signals. Adjust the **dials** so that you can see at least one **complete cycle** of each wave.

3) **Change** the **distance** between the microphone and loudspeaker so that the **peaks** of one wave **line up** with the **troughs** of the other wave (i.e. the waves are **out of phase** — see p.74) and then **measure** the distance between the microphone and loudspeaker.

4) Calculate the **frequency** of the wave by measuring the **period** of the wave from the oscilloscope display and using it in $f = \frac{1}{T}$ (see p.66). The **resolution** of the oscilloscope will be **better** than the resolution of the signal generator, so measuring and calculating the frequency this way will give you a **smaller uncertainty** than just reading the frequency from the signal generator.

Microphone · 2-beam Oscilloscope · Signal generator · Loudspeaker · Ruler

5) Move the microphone **away from** (or **towards**) the loudspeaker so that the microphone's corresponding wave on the oscilloscope **moves** one **full wavelength** along the signal generator's wave — the peaks of one wave and the troughs of the other wave will **line up** again. Measure the **new** distance between the microphone and loudspeaker.

6) The **difference** in your two recorded distances is equal to the **wavelength** of the sound wave.

7) Repeat steps 5-6 and use your results to find a **mean value** for the distance moved by the microphone each time (i.e. the **wavelength**). Then use the equation $v = f\lambda$ to find the value for the **speed of sound**.

Practice Questions

Q1 Define and give the units of the frequency, displacement, amplitude, speed and period of a wave.

Q2 Write down the wave equation.

Q3 Describe an experiment involving a 2-beam oscilloscope, a loudspeaker and a microphone to measure the speed of sound.

Exam Question

Q1 An oscilloscope has the gain set to 2.0 volts/div and a timebase set to 3.0 ms/div. It is displaying the trace of a wave that has a wave speed of 280 ms⁻¹.
   a) State the maximum voltage of the trace. [1 mark]
   b) Calculate the frequency and wavelength of the wave. [5 marks]

volts/div

s/div

Hope you haven't phased out...

Make sure you know what all the waves terms (amplitude, frequency etc.) mean — or this section could get confusing...

Types of Wave

Get a long spring and have a go at making different waves. Or sit there beeping pretending to be a microwave.

In **Transverse Waves**, **Vibration** is at Right Angles to the **Direction** of Travel

1) All **electromagnetic waves** are **transverse**. Other examples of transverse waves are ripples on water or waves on strings.

2) There are **two** main ways of **drawing** transverse waves:

They can be shown as **graphs of displacement against distance along the path of the wave.**

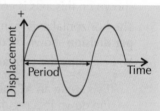

Or, they can be shown as graphs of **displacement against time** for a point as the wave passes.

Displacements **upwards** from the centre line are given a **+ sign**. Displacements downwards are given a **– sign**.

3) Both sorts of graph often give the **same shape** (a **sine wave**), so make sure you check out the label on the **x-axis**.

4) You can work out what **direction** a point on a wave is moving in when given a snapshot of the wave.

Example: Look at the snapshot of the wave on the right. Which direction is point A on the wave moving in?

1) Look at which **direction** the wave is **travelling** in — here the wave is moving from **left** to **right**.

2) The displacement of the wave **just to the left** of point A is **greater** than point A's. So as the wave travels along, point A will need to move **upwards** to have that displacement. (If the displacement to the left was less than point A's, point A would need to move down.)

In **Longitudinal Waves** the **Vibrations** are **Along** the Direction of Travel

The most **common** example of a **longitudinal wave** is **sound**. A sound wave consists of alternate **compressions** and **rarefactions** of the **medium** it's travelling through. (That's why sound can't go through a vacuum.)

Some types of earthquake shock waves are also longitudinal.

The compressions and rarefactions create **pressure variations** in the medium the wave is travelling through — at the points of compression, the **molecules** of the medium are **closer** together, **increasing** the pressure at that point. At the points of rarefaction, the molecules are **further apart**, which means a **lower** pressure at that point.

It's hard to **represent** longitudinal waves **graphically**. You'll usually see them plotted as **displacement** against **time**. These can be **confusing** though, because they look like a **transverse wave**.

Waves Can Be Reflected and Refracted

Reflection — the wave is **bounced back** when it **hits a boundary**. E.g. you can see the reflection of light in mirrors. The reflection of water waves can be demonstrated in a ripple tank.

Refraction — the wave **changes direction** as it enters a **different medium**. The change in direction is a result of the wave slowing down or speeding up.

Tim refused to accept that his long lost twin was just a reflection at an air-water boundary.

Types of Wave

Intensity is a Measure of How Much Energy a Wave is Carrying

1) When you talk about "**brightness**" for light or "**loudness**" for sound, what you really mean is **how much light** or **sound** energy hits your eyes or your ears **per second**.

2) The scientific measure of this is **intensity**.

Intensity is the **rate of flow** of **energy** per **unit area** at **right angles** to the **direction of travel** of the wave. It's measured in Wm⁻².

$$\text{Intensity} = \frac{\text{Power}}{\text{Area}} \qquad I = \frac{P}{A}$$

Example: Light is hitting a 12 cm² piece of paper at right angles to its surface. The power received at the paper is 0.26 W. Calculate the intensity of the light received.

The area of the piece of paper = 12 cm² = 0.0012 m²

Using the equation for intensity:

$I = \frac{P}{A} = \frac{0.26}{0.0012} = 216.6... = \textbf{220 Wm}^{-2}$ **(to 2 s.f.)**

Don't forget to convert from cm² to m² — 1 cm² = 0.00001 m².

Intensity is Proportional to Amplitude Squared

1) This comes from the fact that **intensity** is **proportional** to **energy**, and the energy of a wave depends on the square of the **amplitude**. ➡ **Intensity ∝ (Amplitude)²**

2) From this you can tell that for a **vibrating source** it takes four times as much energy to double the size of the vibrations.

All Electromagnetic (EM) Waves Have Some Properties In Common

1) All EM waves travel in a **vacuum** at a **speed** of **3.00 × 10⁸ ms⁻¹** (to 3 s.f.), and at **slower** speeds in other media.

2) They are **transverse** waves consisting of **vibrating electric** and **magnetic fields**. The **electric** and **magnetic** fields are at **right angles** to each other and to the **direction of travel**.

3) Like all waves, EM waves can be **refracted** (p.78), **reflected** and **diffracted** (p.82-83) and can undergo **interference** (p.74). They also obey $v = f\lambda$ (*v* = velocity, *f* = frequency, λ = wavelength).

4) Like all progressive waves, progressive EM waves **carry energy**.

5) EM waves are transverse so, like all transverse waves, they can be **polarised** (see page 70).

Practice Questions

Q1 Draw a displacement-time graph for a transverse wave. Label a point of maximum displacement and the wavelength of the wave on the graph.

Q2 Draw a displacement-time graph for a point on a longitudinal wave as the wave passes.

Q3 Describe the difference between the vibrations in a transverse wave and a longitudinal wave.

Q4 Describe a longitudinal wave in terms of pressure variations in the medium through which the wave is travelling.

Q5 Give the equation relating power, intensity and area.

Exam Question

Q1 a) A 10.0 W light beam is shone onto a screen with an area of 0.002 m². Calculate the intensity of the light beam on the screen. [1 mark]

b) The intensity of the light on the screen is increased until it is exactly triple the original beam intensity. Which of the following describes the amplitude of the light waves in the beam compared to their original amplitude?

A It is 3 times larger.   B It has halved.   C It is 9 times larger.   D It is √3 times larger.   [1 mark]

So many waves — my arms are getting tired...

Make sure you know the difference between transverse and longitudinal waves — one is up-y down-y and the other is forward-y backward-y. There's nothing quite like a hand-wavey explanation of something (no pun intended...no, really).

Polarisation of Waves

Light waves shake about all over the place. Polarisation is just getting rid of the directions that you don't want.

A *Polarised Wave* Only *Oscillates* in One Direction

1) If you **shake a rope** to make a **wave** you can move your hand **up and down** or **side to side** or in a **mixture** of directions — it still makes a **transverse wave**.

2) But if you try to pass **waves in a rope** through a **vertical fence**, the wave will only get through if the **vibrations are vertical**. The fence filters out vibration in other directions. This is called **polarising** the wave.

Vertical fence

Only up and down vibrations make it through

Vibrations in a mixture of directions.

The wave is polarised.

3) The **plane** in which a wave **vibrates** is called the **plane of polarisation** — e.g. the rope wave was polarised in the **vertical** plane by the fence.

4) Polarising a wave so that it only oscillates in one direction is called **plane polarisation**.

5) Ordinary **light waves** are a mixture of **different directions** of vibration. (The things vibrating are electric and magnetic fields).

Polarisation can only happen for **transverse waves**. So polarising light is one piece of **evidence** that it's a transverse wave.

> For polarised light, the direction of the vibrations (or the plane of polarisation) is always perpendicular to the direction of the propagation of light.

Polarising Filters Only *Transmit* Vibrations in *One Direction*

1) Ordinary **light waves** can be **polarised** using a **polarising filter**.

2) When the transmission axes of the two filters are **aligned**, **all** of the light that passes through the first filter also passes through the second.

3) As you rotate the second filter, the amount of light that passes through the second filter **varies**.

Transmission axes or planes of polarisation (light vibrating this way gets through)

Polarising filters

Unpolarised light

Direction of vibrations

4) As the second filter is rotated, **less** light will get through it as the **vertical** component of the second filter's transmission axis **decreases**. This means the **intensity** of the light getting through the second filter will gradually **decrease**.

5) When the two transmission axes are at **45°** to each other, the intensity will be **half** that getting through the first filter. When they're at **right angles** to each other **no** light will pass through — **intensity is 0**.

> 3D films use polarised light to create depth — the filters in each lens are at right angles to each other so each eye gets a slightly different picture.

Maximum

Light intensity

0

0   90   180   270   360

Angle of rotation of filter from the plane of polarisation, °

6) As you continue turning, the intensity should then begin to **increase** once again.

7) When the two axes **realign** (after a 180° rotation), **all** the light will be able to pass through the second filter again.

When *Light Reflects* it is *Partially Polarised*

1) If you direct a beam of unpolarised light at a reflective surface then view the **reflected ray** through a polarising filter, the intensity of light leaving the filter **changes** with the **orientation** of the filter.

2) The intensity changes because at certain **angles**, light is **partially polarised** when it is **reflected**.

3) This effect is used to remove **unwanted reflections** in photography and in **Polaroid sunglasses** to remove **glare**.

Unpolarised light

Glass block

Partially polarised light

As the polarising filter is rotated, the intensity of light leaving it changes.

When the light reaches the glass block, it is reflected and partially polarised.

Polarisation of Waves

Television and Radio Signals are Polarised

If you look up at the **TV aerials** on people's houses, you'll see that the **rods** (the sticky-out bits) on them are all **horizontal**. This is because **TV signals** are **polarised** by the orientation of the **rods** on the **broadcasting aerial**. To receive a strong signal, you have to **line up** the rods on the **receiving aerial** with the **rods** on the **transmitting aerial** — if they aren't aligned, the signal strength will be lower.

It's the **same** with **radio** — if you try **tuning a radio** and then **moving** the **aerial** around, your signal will **come and go** as the transmitting and receiving aerials go in and out of **alignment**.

Metal Grilles are Used to **Polarise Microwaves**

Polarising filters don't work on **microwaves** — their **wavelength** is too long. Instead, **metal grilles** (squares full of metal wires which are all aligned) are used to polarise them.

You can investigate the polarisation of microwaves using a **microwave transmitter** and a **microwave receiver** linked to a **voltmeter**.

A metal grille

This is the plane of polarisation. It's at right-angles to the wires, unlike with polarising filters where it's parallel to the slits. You don't need to worry about why they're different though.

1) Place a metal grille between the microwave **transmitter** and **receiver** as shown on the right. (Handily, microwave transmitters transmit **polarised** microwaves, so you only need one metal grille.)

2) The intensity of microwaves passing through the grille is at a **maximum** when the direction of the vibration of the microwaves and the plane of polarisation of the grille are **parallel** to each other.

3) As you rotate the grille, the intensity of polarised microwaves able to pass through the grille **decreases**, so the reading on the voltmeter **decreases**.

4) When the plane of polarisation of the metal grille is **perpendicular** with the direction of the vibration of the microwaves, **no signal** will be shown on the voltmeter.

Metal grille - the planes of polarisation of the grille and the microwaves are parallel

Microwave transmitter transmitting polarised waves

Microwave receiver (receives polarised waves)

Voltmeter

Polarised microwaves (direction of vibrations)

Microwaves with slightly reduced amplitudes

The **intensity** drops to **zero** when the plane of polarisation of the metal grille is at **right angles** to the plane of polarisation of the microwaves, because the grille is **absorbing their energy**.

Make sure all of your electrical equipment is safely connected before you turn it on — microwave transmitters operate at very high voltages.

Practice Questions

Q1 What is plane polarisation?

Q2 Why can't you polarise sound waves?

Q3 Why do you have to line up transmitting and receiving television aerials?

Exam Question

Q1 Two polarising filters are placed on top of each other and held in front of a source of white unpolarised light.

  a) No light can be seen through the filters. State the angle between the transmission axes of the two filters. [1 mark]

  b) The filters are rotated so that the angle between their transmission axes is 45°. Describe the difference in the intensity of the light once it has passed through both filters compared to the light once it has only passed through the first filter. [1 mark]

Forget polarisation, I need a mental filter...

...to stop me talking rubbish all the time. Polarisation isn't too bad once you get your head around it. It's just a case of filtering out different directions of wave vibrations. Make sure you really know it though as you'll have to be able to explain how both the experiments for polarising light and microwaves work. Doesn't that sound like a barrel of laughs.

Ultrasound Imaging

I wrote these next two pages for you, because I know what you're thinking — 'This is great, but I want to learn about waves in medical imaging. Also, as a side note, I think CGP books are brilliant.' Oh stop, no really, I'm blushing...

Waves are **Reflected** and **Transmitted** at **Interfaces**

1) The **boundary** between two different media is called an **interface**.

2) When a wave passes from one medium to another, some of its **energy** is **reflected** and some of it is **transmitted** — as shown in the diagram.

3) The proportion of energy reflected or transmitted depends on the two media involved. If the media have very **different densities**, most of the energy is **reflected**. If they are quite **similar**, most of the energy is **transmitted**.

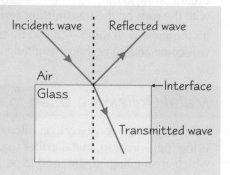

The **Reflection** of **Ultrasound Waves** is Used in **Ultrasound Scans**

1) **Ultrasound waves** are **sound waves** that have too high a **frequency** for humans to **hear**.

2) Ultrasound scans use short pulses of **ultrasound radiation** to form images of the inside of your body.

3) The ultrasound is directed into your body using a **transducer**. If you have air between the transducer and your skin, most of the waves are **reflected** because air has a very **different** density from skin. A **gel** is applied to the skin so there is no air between the transducer and your skin to **increase** the proportion of ultrasound waves that **enter** your body.

4) When the ultrasound waves reach an **interface** inside your body — e.g. between different types of tissue — some of them are **reflected**. A computer attached to the transducer calculates how far from the surface of your skin the interface is by **timing** how long it takes for the reflected waves to **return**.

Sending out ultrasound waves and detecting the reflections is known as a pulse-echo technique.

5) The computer uses the information about the **location** of the boundaries between different tissues to build up an **image** of the inside of your body.

A similar technique is used in **sonar** — e.g. ships send sonar pulses (**ultrasound waves**) down towards the seabed and the pulses are **reflected** back from any **submerged** objects. It can also be used to measure the **speed** of objects.

Shorter Pulses Produce Clearer Images

Ultrasound transducers cannot **transmit** and **receive** pulses at the same time. If **reflected** waves reach the transducer while it is **transmitting**, the information they contain will be **lost** and image **quality** will be reduced. This means:

1) The **pulses** of ultrasound transmitted must be **very short** (a few microseconds long) so that the reflections from nearby interfaces don't reach the transducer before the pulse has ended.

2) The gap between pulses must be **long** (at least 1 millisecond) so that all the reflected waves from one pulse return to the transducer **before** the next pulse is transmitted.

Jack didn't know how to tell Joanna that most of the image quality had been lost.

Ultrasound Imaging

Shorter Wavelengths Produce Clearer Images

Ultrasound scanning can be a really useful technique — but only if the images are **clear**.
The **properties** of the ultrasound **radiation** used has a big effect on the clarity of the images produced.

1) **Shorter** wavelengths **diffract** much **less** than longer wavelengths.
2) This means that the shorter the **wavelength** of the ultrasound, the less the waves **spread out** as they travel and the more **precisely** the location of the interfaces between tissues can be mapped.
3) So ultrasound scanners use waves with a **high frequency** and **short wavelength**.

For more on diffraction of waves, see page 82.

In order for an **object** to be **resolved** (distinguished from other objects), the **wavelength** of the ultrasound wave must be of a **similar size** to the width of the object being resolved.

Example: Ultrasound of frequency 0.95 MHz is used to image a spherical tumour with a diameter of 3.2 mm. If the speed of ultrasound waves in the body is 1540 ms⁻¹, will the tumour be resolved in the ultrasound image?

Find the wavelength of the ultrasound by rearranging $v = f\lambda$:

$$\lambda = \frac{v}{f} = \frac{1540}{0.95 \times 10^6} = 962\,500$$
$$= 1.6210... \times 10^{-3} \text{ m}$$
$$= 1.6210... \text{ mm}$$

Take a look back at p.66 for a reminder on the wave equation.

The wavelength used is approximately half the size of the tumour, so the wavelength and tumour are similar in size. This means it is reasonable to assume that **the tumour will be resolved**.

Practice Questions

Q1 What is an interface?
Q2 What happens to a wave when it reaches an interface?
Q3 How is sonar similar to ultrasound scanning?
Q4 State and explain two things you can do to improve the clarity of an ultrasound image.
Q5 How long does the wavelength of ultrasound used to form an image need to be compared to the size of the object in order to be able to resolve it?

Exam Questions

Q1 Explain how pulse-echo techniques are used to image the inside of a patient's body, including what happens when waves meet an interface between media. [5 marks]

Q2 Explain why a transducer used in medical imaging produces pulses of ultrasound waves with the following properties:

a) A short wavelength. [3 marks]

b) A short pulse length and a long time between pulses. [4 marks]

Ultrasound — Mancunian for 'très bien'

Next time you're watching TV and they show a pregnant woman having her unborn baby scanned, turn to the person you're sat next to and explain how the procedure works. You'll also be able to explain why they put a gel on their stomach first. Just make sure you know the person first before you launch into an explanation about transducers.

Superposition and Coherence

When two waves get together, it can be either really impressive or really disappointing.

Superposition Happens When Two or More Waves Pass Through Each Other

1) At the **instant** the waves **cross**, the **displacements** due to each wave **combine**. Then **each wave** goes on its merry way. You can **see** this if **two pulses** are sent **simultaneously** from each end of a rope.

2) The **principle of superposition** says that when two or more **waves cross**, the **resultant** displacement equals the **vector sum** of the **individual** displacements.

BEFORE   MEETING   AFTER

> "**Superposition**" means "one thing on top of another thing". You can use the same idea in **reverse** — a **complex wave** can be separated out mathematically into **several simple** sine waves of various sizes.

Interference can be Constructive or Destructive

1) When two or more waves **superpose** with each other, the effect is called **interference**.

2) A **crest** plus a **crest** gives a **bigger crest**. A **trough** plus a **trough** gives a **bigger trough**. These are both examples of **constructive interference**.

3) A **crest** plus a **trough** of **equal size** gives... **nothing**. The two displacements **cancel each other out** completely. This is called **destructive interference**.

4) If the **crest** and the **trough** aren't the **same size**, then the destructive interference **isn't total**. For the interference to be **noticeable**, the two **amplitudes** should be **nearly equal**.

> Graphically, you can superimpose waves by adding the individual displacements at each point along the x-axis, and then plotting them.

In Phase Means In Step — Two Points In Phase Interfere Constructively

1) Two points on a wave are **in phase** if they are both at the **same point** in the **wave cycle**. Points in phase have the **same displacement** and **velocity**.

2) On the graph on the right, points **A** and **B** are **in phase**; points **A** and **C** are **out of phase**.

3) It's mathematically **handy** to show one **complete cycle** of a wave as an **angle of 360° (2π radians)**.

4) **Two points** with a **phase difference** of **zero** or a **multiple of 360°** are **in phase**.

5) **Points** with a **phase difference** of odd-number multiples of **180° (π radians)** are **exactly out of phase**.

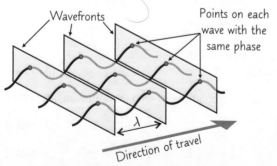

Wavefronts

Points on each wave with the same phase

λ

Direction of travel

6) You can also talk about two **different waves** being **in phase**. **In practice** this usually happens because **both** waves came from the **same oscillator**. In **other** situations there will nearly always be a **phase difference** between two waves.

7) Two or more waves that are **coherent** (see below), **in phase** and travelling in the **same direction** will have **wavefronts**. These are imaginary planes that cut **across** all the waves, joining up all the **points** that are **in phase** with each other. The **distance** between each wavefront is equal to one **wavelength**, i.e. each wavefront is at the same point in the **cycle**.

To Get Interference Patterns the Two Sources Must Be Coherent

Interference **still happens** when you're observing waves of **different wavelength** and **frequency** — but it happens in a **jumble**. In order to get clear **interference patterns**, the two or more sources must be **coherent**.

> **Coherent** sources — they have the **same wavelength** and **frequency** and a **fixed phase difference** between them.

Superposition and Coherence

Constructive or Destructive Interference Depends on the Path Difference

1) Whether you get **constructive** or **destructive** interference at a **point** depends on how **much further one wave** has travelled than the **other wave** to get to that point (assuming the sources are coherent and in phase).

2) The **amount** by which the path travelled by one wave is **longer** than the path travelled by the other wave is called the **path difference**.

3) At **any point an equal distance** from both sources you will get **constructive interference**. You also get constructive interference at any point where the **path difference** is a **whole number of wavelengths**, because the waves arrive at the same point **in phase**. At points where the path difference is an odd number of **half wavelengths**, the waves arrive **out of phase** and you get **destructive interference**.

Constructive interference occurs when:

$$\text{path difference} = n\lambda \quad \text{(where } n \text{ is an integer)}$$

Destructive interference occurs when:

$$\text{path difference} = \frac{(2n+1)\lambda}{2} = (n + \tfrac{1}{2})\lambda$$

If the sources are not in phase but are coherent, there will be constructive and destructive interference, but they will not occur at these path differences.

You Can Observe Interference With Sound Waves

1) Connect two **speakers** to the same oscillator (so the sound waves from them are **coherent** and **in phase**) and place them in line with each other.

2) Walk slowly across the room in front of them.

3) You will hear varying volumes of sound. At the points where the sound is **loudest**, the **path difference** is a **whole** wavelength.

4) The sound will be quietest at points where the path difference is an **odd** number of **half wavelengths**.

You may still hear some sound at the quietest points due to sound being reflected off walls and around the room.

Practice Questions

Q1 What is the principle of superposition?

Q2 If two points on a wave have a phase difference of 1440°, are they in phase?

Q3 What is a wavefront?

Q4 If there was a path difference of 5λ between two coherent, in phase waves, what kind of interference would occur?

Exam Questions

Q1 a) Two wave sources are coherent. Explain what this means. [2 marks]

b) Explain why you might have difficulty in observing interference patterns in an area affected by two waves from two sources even though the two sources are coherent. [1 mark]

Q2 Two waves from coherent sources meet and interfere. Which row of the table shows the correct type of interference that would occur with the stated phase and path difference? [1 mark]

	Phase Difference	Path Difference	Type of Interference
A	180°	λ	Constructive
B	180°	λ/2	Constructive
C	360°	λ	Destructive
D	360°	λ/2	Constructive

Learn this and you'll be in a super position to pass your exam...   ...I'll get my coat.

A few crucial concepts here: a) interference can be constructive or destructive, b) you get constructive interference when the path difference is a whole number of wavelengths (for sources in phase), c) the sources must be coherent.

TOPIC 5 — WAVES AND PARTICLE NATURE OF LIGHT

Stationary (Standing) Waves

Stationary waves are waves that... er... stand still... well, not still exactly... I mean, well... they don't go anywhere... um...

You get Stationary Waves When a **Progressive Wave** is **Reflected** at a **Boundary**

A stationary wave is the **superposition** of **two progressive waves** with the **same wavelength**, moving in **opposite directions**.

The progressive waves must also have the same speed and frequency.

1) Unlike progressive waves, **no energy** is transmitted by a stationary wave.

2) You can demonstrate stationary waves by attaching a **vibration transducer** at one end of a **stretched string** with the other end fixed. The transducer is given a wave frequency by a **signal generator** and creates that wave by vibrating the string.

3) The wave generated by the vibration transducer is **reflected** back and forth.

4) For most frequencies the resultant **pattern** is a **jumble**. However, if you alter the **signal generator** so the **transducer** produces an **exact number of waves** in the time it takes for a wave to get to the **end** and **back again**, then the **original** and **reflected** waves **reinforce** each other.

5) At these **"resonant frequencies"** you get a **stationary** (or **standing**) **wave** where the **pattern doesn't move** — it just sits there, bobbing up and down. Happy, at peace with the world...

A sitting wave.

Stationary Waves in **Strings** Form **Oscillating "Loops"** Separated by **Nodes**

1) Each particle vibrates at **right angles** to the string.

2) **Nodes** are where the **amplitude** of the vibration is **zero**.

3) **Antinodes** are points of **maximum amplitude**.

4) At resonant frequencies, an **exact number** of **half wavelengths** fits onto the string.

The standing wave above is vibrating at the **lowest possible** resonant frequency (the **fundamental mode of vibration** — also called the **first harmonic**). It has **one "loop"** with a **node at each end**.

This is the **second harmonic**. It is **twice** the **fundamental mode of vibration**. There are two "loops" with a **node** in the **middle** and **one at each end**.

The **third harmonic** is **three times** the fundamental mode of vibration. **1½ wavelengths** fit on the string.

You can **Demonstrate Stationary Waves** with Microwaves and Sounds

Microwaves Reflected Off a Metal Plate Set Up a Stationary Wave

Microwave stationary wave apparatus

You can find the **nodes** and **antinodes** by moving the **probe** between the **transmitter** and **reflecting plate**.

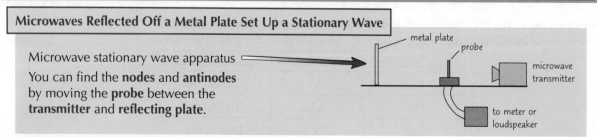

Powder Can Show Stationary Waves in a Tube of Air

Stationary **sound** waves are produced in the **glass tube**.

The lycopodium **powder** (don't worry, you don't need to know what that is) laid along the bottom of the tube is **shaken away** from the **antinodes** but left **undisturbed** at the **nodes**.

Stationary (Standing) Waves

You Can Investigate Factors Affecting the Resonant Frequencies of a String

1) Start by measuring the **mass** (M) and **length** (L) of strings of different types using a **mass balance** and a ruler. Then find the **mass per unit length** of each string (μ) using:

$$\mu = \frac{M}{L}$$ The units of μ are kgm⁻¹

string fixed to vibration transducer   length, /   pulley

signal generator   string

bench   masses

tension, T

2) Set up the apparatus shown in the diagram with one of your strings. Record μ, measure and record the **length** (/) and work out the **tension** (T) using:

$$T = mg$$ where m is the total mass of the masses in kg

A vibration transducer is connected to a signal generator that tells it the frequency of the wave you want. A vibrating plate on the transducer creates the wave.

3) Turn on the **signal generator** and vary the frequency until you find the **first harmonic** — i.e. a stationary wave that has a **node** at each end and a single **antinode**. This is the **frequency of the first harmonic, f**.

4) The **wavelength** of the wave, λ, is given by λ = 2/ for the **fundamental mode frequency**. The **frequency, f**, and the **velocity** of the wave, v, for the first harmonic are:

You can investigate how the **length, tension** or **mass per unit length** of the string affects the **resonant frequency** by:

$$f = \frac{1}{2l}\sqrt{\frac{T}{\mu}}$$ $$v = \sqrt{\frac{T}{\mu}}$$

The equation for v is true for _any_ transverse wave on a string.

1) Keeping the string **type** (μ) and the **tension** (T) in it the same and altering the **length** (/). Do this by moving the **vibration transducer** towards or away from the pulley. Find the **first harmonic** again, and record f against /.

2) Keeping the string **type** (μ) and **length** (/) the same and **adding** or **removing masses** to change the tension (T). Find the first harmonic again and record f against T.

3) Keeping the **length** (/) and **tension** (T) the same, but using **different string** samples to vary μ. Find the first harmonic and record f against μ.

You can do this experiment with a different harmonic — just remember to use the same one throughout the experiment. You won't be able to use the equation for f though — this is just for the fundamental mode of vibration.

You should find the following from your investigation:

1) The **longer** the string, the **lower** the resonant frequency
   — because the **half wavelength** at the resonant frequency is longer.

2) The **heavier** (i.e. the more mass per unit length) the string, the **lower** the resonant frequency — because waves travel more **slowly** down the string. For a given **length** a **lower** wave speed, v, makes a **lower** frequency, f.

3) The **looser** the string the **lower** the resonant frequency — because waves travel more **slowly** down a **loose** string.

Practice Questions

Q1 How do stationary waves form?

Q2 Sketch the first three fundamental modes of vibration of a standing wave on three different diagrams.

Q3 At four times the frequency of the first harmonic, how many half wavelengths would fit on a violin string?

Q4 How does the displacement of a particle at one antinode compare to that of a particle at another antinode?

Exam Questions

Q1 A string of fixed length 2.8 m is oscillating at its fundamental mode of vibration. Calculate the mass of the string if the standing wave has velocity 16 ms⁻¹ and the tension on the string is 3.2 N. [2 marks]

Q2 A stationary wave at the first harmonic frequency, 10 Hz (to 2 s.f.), is formed on a stretched string of length 1.2 m.

a) Calculate the wavelength of the wave. [2 marks]

b) The tension is doubled whilst all other factors remain constant. The frequency is adjusted to once more find the first harmonic of the string. Calculate the new frequency of the first harmonic. [3 marks]

c) Explain how the variation of amplitude along the string differs from that of a progressive wave. [2 marks]

Don't get tied up in knots...

Remember — the lowest frequency at which a standing wave is formed is the fundamental mode of vibration.

Refractive Index

The stuff on the next two pages explains why your legs look short in a swimming pool.

Refraction Occurs When the Medium a Wave is Travelling in Changes

Refraction is the way a wave **changes direction** as it enters a **different medium**. The change
in direction is a result of the wave **slowing down** or **speeding up**. You can tell if the wave is
speeding up or slowing down by the way it **bends towards** or **away** from the normal.

1) If a light ray bends **towards** the normal — it is **slowing** down. The ray is going
   from a **less** optically dense material to a **more** optically dense material.

2) If the ray bends **away** from the normal — the wave is **speeding up**. It is going
   from an optically **denser** material to a **less** optically dense material.

The more optically dense material will have a higher refractive index (see below).

3) The speed changes because the **wavelength** of the wave is changing and the **frequency** stays **constant** ($v = f\lambda$).

> If light travels from a **less** optically dense material to a **more** optically dense material,
> the wave **slows down**, the wavelength **decreases** and the frequency stays the **same**.

The Refractive Index of a Material Measures How Much It Slows Down Light

Light goes fastest in a **vacuum**. It **slows down** in other materials, because it **interacts** with the particles in them.
The more **optically dense** a material is, the more light **slows down** when it enters it.

> The **refractive index** of a material, n, is the **ratio** between the **speed**
> of light in a **vacuum**, c, and the speed of light in that **material**, v.

$$n = \frac{c}{v}$$

$c = 3.00 \times 10^8$ ms^{-1}.

The speed of light in air is only a tiny bit smaller than c. So you can assume the refractive index of air is 1.

Snell's Law uses Angles to Calculate the Refractive Index

1) The **angle** the **incoming light** makes to the **normal** is called the **angle of incidence**, θ_1.
   The **angle** the **refracted ray** makes with the **normal** is the **angle of refraction**, θ_2.

2) The light is crossing a **boundary**, going from a medium with
   refractive index n_1 to a medium with refractive index n_2.

3) When light enters an **optically denser** medium it is refracted **towards** the normal.

4) n_1, n_2, θ_1 and θ_2 are related by **Snell's law**: $n_1 \sin \theta_1 = n_2 \sin \theta_2$

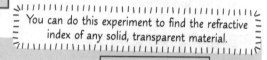

You can use a **ray box** to find the **refractive index** of a glass block:

You can do this experiment to find the refractive index of any solid, transparent material.

1) Place a glass block on a piece of paper and draw around it.

2) Use the ray box to shine a beam of light into the glass block. Turn off any
   other lights so you can see the path of the light beam through the block clearly.

3) **Trace** the path of the **incoming** and **outgoing** beams of light either side of the block.

4) Remove the block and join up the two paths you've drawn with a
   straight line that follows the path the light beam took through the
   glass block. You should be able to see from your drawing how the
   path of the ray **bent** when entering and leaving the block.

5) Measure the angles of incidence (θ_1) and refraction (θ_2) where the light enters and exits the block. Air is less
   optically dense than glass, so as the light **enters** the glass block it **bends towards** the normal ($\theta_1 > \theta_2$) as it
   slows down. The beam should bend **away** from the normal as it **exits** the block ($\theta_2 > \theta_1$) and **speeds up**.

6) Rearrange Snell's law to make the refractive index of the
   material the subject, and substitute in $n = 1$ for **air** and the
   values you found for θ_1 and θ_2 to calculate a value for n.

   Alternatively, you could plot a graph of $\sin\theta_1$ against $\sin\theta_2$. The gradient of the graph will be equal to the refractive index of the material.

7) The **percentage uncertainty** (see p.10) in your measurements
   for θ_1 and θ_2 will be **smaller** for **larger angles**, so it's better to do the experiment at
   large angles and then **repeat** the experiment to find an **average** of your results.

8) Your result should be more **precise** (see p.12) if you use a **narrower** beam of light as the **uncertainty** in the
   position of the beam will be lower.

Refractive Index

When the Angle of *Refraction* is a *Right Angle*, the Angle of *Incidence* is *Critical*

When light **goes from** an optically dense material into an optically **less dense** material (e.g. glass to air), interesting things can start to happen.

Shine a ray of light at a **glass to air** boundary, then gradually **increase** the angle of incidence. As you increase the angle of incidence, the angle of **refraction** gets closer and closer to **90°**. Eventually the angle of incidence, θ_1 reaches a **critical angle C** for which the angle of refraction, $\theta_2 = 90°$. The light is refracted **along the boundary**.

At angles of incidence **greater than C**, refraction is **impossible**. That means **all** the light is reflected back into the material. This effect is called **total internal reflection**.

For light hitting a **material-to-air boundary** (assuming the material is more optically **dense**) at the critical angle, **Snell's law** simplifies to become:

$$\sin C = \frac{1}{n}$$

This happens because $n_{air} = 1$ and $\sin(90°) = 1$. n is the refractive index of the material.

You can Investigate *Critical Angles* and *Total Internal Reflection* with *Glass Blocks*

1) Shine a light ray into the **curved face** of a semi-circular glass block so that it always enters at **right angles** to the edge — this means the ray won't **refract** as it enters the block, just when it leaves from the straight edge.

2) Vary the angle of **incidence**, θ_1, until the light beam refracts so much that it exits the block along the **straight edge**. This angle of incidence is the **critical angle**, C, for glass-air boundary. ⟹ You can rearrange the formula for the critical angle above and put in your value for C to find the refractive index of the block.

3) If you increase the angle of incidence so it's **greater** than C, you'll find the ray is reflected from the straight edge of the block.

Here the angle of incidence is less than the critical angle

Here the angle of incidence is equal to the critical angle

Here the angle of incidence is greater than the critical angle.

Practice Questions

Q1 What happens to the wavelength of light as it passes from water into air?

Q2 Why does light go fastest in a vacuum and slow down in other media?

Q3 Diamond has a higher refractive index than sapphire. Is total internal reflection possible for light travelling in sapphire when it meets a sapphire-diamond interface?

Q4 Describe an experiment you could do to determine the critical angle of a boundary between a material and air.

Exam Questions

Q1 a) Light travels in diamond at 1.24×10^8 ms^{-1}. What is the refractive index of diamond? [1 mark]

b) Calculate the angle of refraction if light strikes a facet of a diamond ring at an angle of exactly 50° to the normal of the air/diamond boundary. [2 marks]

Q2 An adjustable underwater spotlight is placed on the floor of an aquarium tank. When the light points upwards at a steep angle a beam comes through the surface of the water into the air, and the tank is dimly lit. When the spotlight is placed at a shallower angle, no light comes up through the water surface, and the tank is brightly lit.

a) Explain what is happening. [2 marks]

b) It is found that the beam into the air disappears when the spotlight is pointed at any angle of less than 41.25° to the floor. Calculate the refractive index of water. [2 marks]

Critical angles are never happy...

Total internal reflection doesn't sound like the most riveting subject, but it's super useful. Optical fibres wouldn't work without it, and we use them for all sorts of things — broadband connections, telephone cables, making things sparkly...

Lenses

Lenses are pretty useful — they're used in glasses to help you see, they're used in telescopes to help you see, they're used in magnifying glasses to help you see, they're used in your eyes to help... you get the picture.

Converging Lenses Bring Light Rays Together

1) **Lenses** change the **direction** of light rays by **refraction**.
2) **Converging** lenses bulge **outwards**.
3) Rays **parallel** to the **principal axis** of the lens converge onto a point called the **principal focus**. Parallel rays that **aren't** parallel to the principal axis converge somewhere else on the **focal plane** (see diagram).
4) The **focal length**, *f*, is the distance between the **lens axis** and the **focal plane**.
5) *f* is **positive** for a **converging** lens because it is **in front of** the lens.

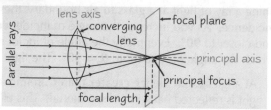

Diverging Lenses Spread Light Rays Out

1) **Diverging** lenses cave **inwards**.
2) The **principal focus** of a diverging lens is at a point **behind** the lens.
3) The principal focus is the point that rays from a **distant** object, assumed to be parallel to the principal axis, **appear** to have come from. The dotted lines in the diagram show **virtual rays**. The light **doesn't** actually follow this path, but **appears** to have done so.
4) The **focal length**, *f*, is the distance between the **lens axis** and the **principal focus**.
5) *f* is **negative** for a **diverging** lens because it is **behind** the lens.

Images can be Real or Virtual

1) A **real image** is formed when light rays from a point on an object are made to **pass through** another point in space. The light rays are **actually there**, and the image can be **captured** on a **screen**.
2) A **virtual image** is formed when light rays from a point on an object **appear** to have come from another point in space. The light rays **aren't really where the image appears to be**, so the image **can't** be captured on a screen.
3) Converging lenses can form both **real** and **virtual** images, depending on where the object is. If the object is **further** than the **focal length** away from the lens, the image is **real**. If the object's **closer**, the image is **virtual**.
4) To work out where an image formed by a converging lens will appear, you can draw a **ray diagram**. Draw **two rays** from the same point on the object (the top is best) one **parallel** to the principal axis that passes through the **principal focus**, and one passing through the **centre** of the lens that **doesn't get refracted** (bent). The image will form where the **two rays meet** if the image is real. If the rays don't meet, the image is **virtual**. **Extend** the rays back (draw **virtual rays**) to locate where the two rays appear to have **come from**:

If an object sits on the principal axis, so will the image.

In the diagram, **u** = distance between object and lens axis, **v** = distance between image and lens axis (**positive** if image is **real**, **negative** if image is **virtual**), **f** = focal length.

5) A diverging lens will **always** form a virtual image — the **position** of the **object** in relation to the **focal length** will not affect the **type** of image formed.
6) To draw a **ray diagram** for a diverging lens, draw **two rays** from the same point on the object. One must pass through the **centre** of the lens without getting refracted. The other travels **parallel** to the **principal axis** until it meets the centre of the lens. Then it **refracts** so that it **appears** to come from the **principal focus**. The image will form where the real and virtual rays **meet**.
7) The values **u**, **v** and **f** are related by the **lens equation**:

$$\frac{1}{f} = \frac{1}{u} + \frac{1}{v}$$

This equation only works for thin lenses.

Lenses

Power Tells You How Much a Lens Bends Light

1) You can calculate the **power** of a lens, which tells you the lens' ability to **bend light**. The higher the power, the more the lens will **refract** light.

$$P = \frac{1}{f}$$ where P is the power of the lens in dioptres (D).

2) Imagine you have two or more **thin** lenses in a line, with their principal axes lined up. If the lenses are **touching** or are very **close together**, the **total power** of the lenses is found by just **adding** all the powers together — how simple.

$$P = P_1 + P_2 + P_3 + ...$$

Example: An image of Mabel the cow is being projected onto a screen 80 cm from a 3.25 D converging lens. How far must the picture slide of Mabel be from the lens?

$P = \frac{1}{f} = 3.25$ D, and the image must be real as it is captured on a screen, so $v = 80$ cm $= 0.8$ m.

Rearrange the lens equation: $\frac{1}{u} = \frac{1}{f} - \frac{1}{v} = 3.25 - \frac{1}{0.8}$

$= 3.25 - 1.25 = 2$

$u = \frac{1}{2} = 0.5$ m,

so the slide must be **0.5 m** from the lens.

A Lens Can Produce a Magnified Image

Magnification is a ratio and so has no units.

The magnification, m, of an image can be calculated in two different ways. They are:

$$m = \frac{\text{image height}}{\text{object height}}$$

$$m = \frac{v}{u}$$

Practice Questions

Q1 Define the focal length and power of a converging lens.

Q2 Draw a ray diagram for the converging lens and object shown on the right. State whether the image formed is real or virtual.

Q3 State whether real or virtual images are produced by diverging lenses.

Q4 Write an equation to show how the object distance (u), image distance (v) and focal length of a thin lens (f) are related.

Q5 A diverging lens has a magnification of 3.4. An image of an object created by the lens is 12.8 cm wide. How wide is the object?

Exam Questions

Q1 a) Define the principal focus of a converging lens. [1 mark]

b) An object was placed 0.20 m in front of a converging lens of focal length 0.15 m. Calculate how far behind the lens the image was formed. [2 marks]

Q2 The length of a seed is 12.5 mm. A lens is placed in front of the seed, so that the principal axis of the lens is parallel to the seed. An image of the seed is projected onto a screen. The image has a length of 47.2 mm.

a) Calculate the linear magnification of the lens. [1 mark]

b) If the seed is 4.0 mm from the lens, calculate how far the screen is from the lens. [2 marks]

c) Calculate the power of the lens in dioptres. [2 marks]

d) A second lens is placed directly after the first lens. The focal length of the combined lenses is 0.22 cm. Calculate the power of the second lens. [2 marks]

The physics is real, the fun is virtual...

Ray diagrams might look complicated, but once you've practised them a few times it'll all be a doddle. Or a doodle...

Diffraction

Diffraction is some funky stuff — it's all about waves squeezing through spaces and then spreading out. Kind of like whipped cream from a can. Actually, it's nothing like that... read the pages and learn some stuff.

Waves Go **Round Corners** and **Spread out** of Gaps

The way that **waves spread out** as they come through a **narrow gap** or go round obstacles is called **diffraction**. **All** waves diffract, but it's not always easy to observe. The amount of diffraction depends on the **size of the gap** in comparison to the **wavelength** of the wave.

You Can Use a **Ripple Tank** to Investigate **Diffraction**

1) **Ripple tanks** are shallow tanks of water that you can generate a wave in.

2) This is done by an **oscillating paddle**, which continually dips into the water and creates regular waves with straight, parallel wavefronts.

> Take a look back at p.74 for a reminder on what a wavefront is.

3) Objects are then placed into the ripple tank to create a **barrier** with a **gap** in the middle of it.

4) This gap can be varied to see the effects this has on how the waves spread through the tank.

When the gap is **a lot bigger** than the **wavelength**, diffraction is **unnoticeable**.

You get **noticeable diffraction** through a gap **several** wavelengths wide.

You get the **most diffraction** when the gap is **the same** size as the **wavelength**.

As the gap decreases, the diffraction becomes more noticeable until the gap becomes too small and the water waves cannot pass through it anymore. The waves are then **reflected** back on themselves.

When **sound** passes through a **doorway**, the **size of gap** and the **wavelength** are usually roughly **equal**, so a **lot** of **diffraction** occurs. That's why you have no trouble **hearing** someone through an **open door** to the next room, even if the other person is out of your **line of sight**. The reason that you can't **see** him or her is that when **light** passes through the doorway, it is passing through a **gap** around a **hundred million times bigger** than its wavelength — the amount of diffraction is **tiny**.

Diffraction can be **Explained** Using **Huygens' Construction**

1) Huygens developed a **general model** of the propagation of **waves** in what is now known as **Huygens' construction**:

> **HUYGENS' CONSTRUCTION:** Every point on a wavefront may be considered to be a **point source** of secondary wavelets that spread out in the forward direction at the speed of the wave. The **new wavefront** is the surface that is **tangential** to all of these **secondary wavelets**.

This diagram shows how this works:

Light travelling in this direction
wavefront → point sources
← secondary wavelets
← new wavefront

2) Huygens' construction can be used to explain the shape of the wavefronts as light travels through a **slit**. The **secondary wavelets** that pass through the slit are what produce the curve of the **new wavefront** emerging from the slit.

Light travelling in this direction

The wavelets from these point sources don't pass through the slit

secondary wavelets — new wavefront

Diffraction

You Get **Diffraction** Around an **Obstacle** Too

When a wave meets an **obstacle**, you get diffraction around the edges. Behind the obstacle is a '**shadow**', where the wave is blocked. The **wider** the obstacle compared with the wavelength of the wave, the less diffraction you get, and so the **longer** the shadow.

This can also be shown using Huygens' construction:

This diagram looks more complicated than the ones on p.82, but don't panic — exactly the same principles apply here.

Light travelling in this direction

With **Light Waves** you get a Pattern of **Light** and **Dark Fringes**

1) If the **wavelength** of a **light wave** is roughly similar to the size of the **aperture**, you get a **diffraction pattern** of light and dark fringes.

2) The pattern has a **bright central fringe** with alternating **dark and bright fringes** on either side of it.

3) The **spread** of the diffraction pattern depends on the **relative sizes** of the wavelength and the slit width. The **longer** the wavelength is **compared** to the **width** of the slit, the **wider** the diffraction pattern.

light · slit · screen · pattern on screen

You need to use a coherent light source (page 74) for this experiment.

Practice Questions

Q1 What is diffraction?

Q2 For a long time some scientists argued that light couldn't be a wave because it did not seem to diffract. Suggest why they might have got this impression.

Q3 Light passes through a slit that is a few wavelengths wide. Use Huygens' construction to explain the shape of the wavefronts of the light as they emerge from the other side of the slit.

Q4 Sketch what happens when plane waves meet an obstacle about as wide as one wavelength.

Q5 Light passing through a slit produces a diffraction pattern. State what effect decreasing the wavelength of the light would have on the width of the diffraction pattern.

Exam Questions

Q1 A mountain lies directly between you and a radio transmitter.
Explain, with the use of a diagram, why you can pick up long-wave radio broadcasts from the transmitter but not short-wave radio broadcasts.   [3 marks]

Q2 Describe how you would use a ripple tank to investigate how the wavelength of a wave and the size of the gap a wave travels through relates to the amount of diffraction which occurs. Comment on when maximum diffraction will be seen.   [3 marks]

Even hiding behind a mountain, you can't get away from long-wave radio...

Unfortunately "Bay FM" don't transmit using long wave radio. So as I'm giving the singing-in-the-car performance of my life, I go over a hill and the signal cuts out. Where's diffraction when I need it then hmm? How will I ever become famous? Diffraction crops up again in stuff like quantum physics so make sure you really understand it.

Diffraction Gratings

What could possibly be more exciting than shining a laser through two slits? Shining a laser through more than two slits of course. Jeez, ask a stupid question...

Interference Patterns Get **Sharper** When You Diffract Through **More Slits**

1) You saw on pages 74-75 that **two sources** that produce waves that are **coherent** and **in phase** will result in an **interference pattern** (alternating bands of constructive and destructive interference). If you are using **light waves**, you can pass one **monochromatic** (one wavelength) **beam of light** through **two slits**. The slits are cut into the **same** piece of material, so that the wave passes through them at the **same time**. The light **diffracts** at both slits, producing two coherent sources of light. The interference pattern is made up of alternating **dark bands** and **light bands**.

2) You can repeat this experiment with **more than two equally spaced** slits. You get basically the **same shaped** pattern as for two slits — but the **bright bands** are **brighter** and **narrower** and the **dark areas** between are **darker**.

3) When **monochromatic light** is passed through a **grating**, which has **hundreds** of slits per millimetre, the interference pattern is **really sharp** because there are so **many beams reinforcing** the **pattern**.

4) Sharper fringes make for more **precise** measurements as they are easier to tell apart and so are **easier** to measure.

screen

diffraction grating

Measurements Can be Made from **Interference Patterns**

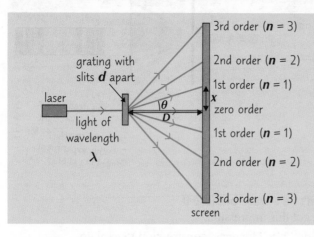

grating with slits **d** apart

laser

light of wavelength **λ**

3rd order (**n** = 3)

2nd order (**n** = 2)

1st order (**n** = 1)

x

zero order

1st order (**n** = 1)

2nd order (**n** = 2)

3rd order (**n** = 3)

screen

1) For monochromatic light, all of the maxima are sharp lines. (It's different for white light — see the next page).

2) This means the distance between the maxima can be easily measured (**fringe width**).

3) There's a line of **maximum brightness** at the centre called the **zero order** line.

4) The lines just **either side** of the central one are called **first order lines**. The **next pair out** are called **second order** lines and so on.

If the grating has N slits per metre, then the slit spacing, d, is just 1/N metres.

Measuring the Wavelength of Light using a Diffraction Grating

1) Position a **laser** (or other monochromatic light source) in front of a **diffraction grating** so that the light travels through the grating and creates an interference pattern on a **flat wall** or **screen** a few metres away.

2) Measure the **distance, D**, between the diffraction grating and the wall.

3) Measure the **distance, x**, between the **zero order maximum** and the **1st order maximum** for both sides and take an **average** of the two readings.

Make sure the light is travelling at right angles to the diffraction grating and wall.

4) Using the **fringe width, x**, and the distance to the wall, **D**, the angle the 1st order fringe makes with the zero order line can be calculated using **small angle approximations**.

Don't forget to set your calculator to radians when using this equation.

$$\tan \theta \approx \theta \text{ and } \tan \theta = \frac{x}{D}, \text{ so } \theta \approx \frac{x}{D}$$

The value for d is usually given on the grating. Don't forget that n = 1 for the zero order line.

5) You can then use the following **equation** to **calculate** the **wavelength** of light: $d \sin \theta = n\lambda$

6) **Repeat** the measurements for more **order lines** to find an **average** for the wavelength.

7) Repeat the experiment for a diffraction grating that has a **different distance** between the **slits**.

Diffraction Gratings

You can Draw General Conclusions from d sin θ = nλ

1) If λ is **bigger**, sin θ is **bigger**, and so θ is **bigger**. This means that the larger the **wavelength**, the more the pattern will **spread out**.

2) If *d* is **bigger**, sin θ is **smaller**. This means that the **coarser** the grating, the **less** the pattern will **spread out**.

3) Values of sin θ greater than **1** are **impossible**. So if for a certain *n* you get a result of **more than 1** for sin θ you know that that order **doesn't exist**.

Shining White Light Through a Diffraction Grating Produces Spectra

1) **White light** is really a **mixture** of **colours**. If you **diffract** white light through a **grating** then the patterns due to **different wavelengths** within the white light are **spread out** by **different** amounts.

2) Each **order** in the pattern becomes a **spectrum**, with **red** on the **outside** and **violet** on the **inside**. The **zero order maximum** stays **white** because all the wavelengths just pass straight through.

| second order | first order | zero order (white) | first order | second order |

3) **Astronomers** and **chemists** often need to study spectra to help identify elements. They use diffraction gratings rather than prisms because they're **more accurate**.

4) Another example of white light being **split** into a spectrum due to diffraction can be seen on **CDs** and **DVDs**. There are **grooves** etched into the **reflective surface**, which causes the light to **diffract**. Constructive interference occurs at different points for light with different wavelengths, so you end up seeing a **rainbow pattern**.

Practice Questions

Q1 Why do more slits in a diffraction grating lead to a sharper diffraction pattern?

Q2 What is the formula for finding the wavelength of light incident on a diffraction grating?

Q3 A beam of light is diffracted through a diffraction grating. State what will happen to the diffraction pattern if the wavelength of the light decreases.

Q4 Describe an experiment to find the wavelength of monochromatic light using a diffraction grating.

Exam Questions

Q1 Yellow laser light of wavelength 6.00×10^{-7} m is transmitted through a diffraction grating of 4.0×10^5 lines per metre.

a) State the angle to the normal where the first and second order bright lines are seen. [4 marks]

b) State whether there is a fifth order line. Explain your answer. [1 mark]

Q2 Visible, monochromatic light is transmitted through a diffraction grating of 3.70×10^5 lines per metre. The first order maximum is at an angle of 14.2° to the incident beam.

Calculate the wavelength of the incident light. [2 marks]

Oooooooooooooo — pretty patterns...

Yes, it's the end of another beautiful topic. Three important points for you to take away — the more slits you have, the sharper the image, monochromatic light leads to sharp fringes and one lovely equation to get to know. Make sure you get everything in this topic — there's some good stuff waiting in the next one and I wouldn't want you to be distracted.

Light — Wave or Photon?

You probably already thought light was a bit weird — but oh no... being a wave that travels at the fastest speed possible isn't enough for light — it has to go one step further and act like a particle too...

Light Behaves Like a **Wave...** or a **Stream of Particles**

1) In the **late nineteenth century**, if you asked what light was, scientists would happily show you lots of nice experiments showing how light must be a **wave**.

2) Light produces **interference** and **diffraction** patterns — **alternating bands** of **dark** and **light**. These patterns can **only** be explained using **waves**.

3) That was all fine and dandy... until the **photoelectric effect** (p.88), which mucked up everything. The only way you could explain this effect was if light acted as a **particle** — called a **photon**.

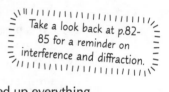

Take a look back at p.82-85 for a reminder on interference and diffraction.

A **Photon** is a **Quantum** of **EM Radiation**

1) When Max Planck was investigating **black body radiation** (don't worry — you don't need to know about that right now), he suggested that **EM waves** can **only** be **released** in **discrete packets**, called **quanta**. A single packet of **EM radiation** is called a **quantum**.

The **energy carried** by one of these **wave-packets** had to be:

$$E = hf = \frac{hc}{\lambda}$$

where h = Planck constant = 6.63×10^{-34} Js, f = frequency (Hz), λ = wavelength (m) and c = speed of light in a vacuum = 3.00×10^8 ms^{-1}

2) So, the **higher** the **frequency** of the electromagnetic radiation, the more **energy** its wave-packets carry.

3) **Einstein** went **further** by suggesting that **EM waves** (and the energy they carry) can only **exist** in discrete packets. He called these wave-packets **photons**.

4) He believed that a photon acts as a **particle**, and will either transfer **all** or **none** of its energy when interacting with another particle, e.g. an electron.

5) Photons have **no charge** — they are **neutral**, like neutrons.

Electrons in **Atoms** Exist in **Discrete Energy Levels**

1) **Electrons** in an **atom** can **only exist** in certain **well-defined energy levels**. Each level is given a **number**, with n = 1 representing the **ground state**.

2) Electrons can **move down** energy levels by **emitting** a photon.

3) Since these **transitions** are between **definite energy levels**, the **energy** (and therefore the **frequency**) of **each photon** emitted can **only** take a **certain allowed value**.

4) The diagram on the right shows the **energy levels** for **atomic hydrogen**.

5) The **energies involved** are **so tiny** that it makes sense to use a more **appropriate unit** than the **joule**. When you **accelerate** an electron between two electrodes, it transfers some electrical potential energy (eV) into kinetic energy.

$$eV = \frac{1}{2}mv^2$$

e is the size of the charge on an electron: 1.60×10^{-19} C. See page 43.

6) The **electronvolt (eV)** is defined as:

> The **kinetic energy carried** by an **electron** after it has been **accelerated** through a **potential difference of 1 volt**.

So 1 electron volt = $e \times V = 1.60 \times 10^{-19}$ C $\times$ 1 JC^{-1}.

$$\boxed{1 \text{ eV} = 1.60 \times 10^{-19} \text{ J}}$$

7) On the diagram, energies are labelled in **both units** for **comparison's** sake.

8) The **energy** carried by each **photon** is **equal** to the **difference in energies** between the **two levels**. The equation below shows a **transition** between a higher energy level n = 2 where the electrons have energy E_2 and a lower energy level n = 1 with electrons of energy E_1:

$$\Delta E = E_2 - E_1 = hf = \frac{hc}{\lambda}$$

9) Electrons can also **move up** energy levels if they **absorb a photon** with the **exact energy difference** between the two levels. The movement of an electron to a higher energy level is called **excitation**.

The ground state is the lowest energy state of the atom.

LEVEL	ENERGY
n = ∞	zero energy
n = 5	-8.6×10^{-20} J or -0.54 eV
n = 4	-1.4×10^{-19} J or -0.85 eV
n = 3	-2.4×10^{-19} J or -1.5 eV
n = 2	-5.4×10^{-19} J or -3.4 eV
n = 1	-2.2×10^{-18} J or -13.6 eV

transitions

The energies are only negative because of how "zero energy" is defined. Just one of those silly convention things — don't worry about it.

Light — Wave or Photon?

Continuous Spectra Contain All Possible Wavelengths

1) The **spectrum** of **white light** is **continuous**.
2) If you **split** the **light** up with a **prism**, the **colours** all **merge** into each other — there **aren't** any **gaps** in the spectrum.

Decreasing wavelength ⟹

Hot Gases Produce Line Emission Spectra

1) If you heat a gas to a **high temperature**, the **atoms** become excited (one or more of their **electrons** is moved to a **higher** energy level).

2) As electrons within the atoms **fall** back to the **lower energy levels**, they **emit energy** as photons (see previous page).

3) If you **split** the light from a **hot gas** with a **prism** or a **diffraction grating** (see pages 84-85), you get a **line emission spectrum**.

4) A line emission spectrum is seen as a **series** of **bright lines** against a **black background**, as shown above.

5) Each **line** on the spectrum corresponds to a **particular wavelength** of light **emitted** by the source. Since only **certain photon energies** are **allowed**, you only see the **corresponding wavelengths**.

excited gas

prism (or diffraction grating)

Cool Gases Produce Line Absorption Spectra

1) You get a **line absorption spectrum** when **white light** passes through a cool gas and then a **diffraction grating** or **prism**.

2) At **low temperatures**, **most** of the **electrons** in the **gas atoms** will be in their **ground states**.

3) **Photons** of the **correct wavelength** are **absorbed** by the **electrons** to **excite** them to **higher energy levels**.

4) These **wavelengths** are then **missing** from the **continuous spectrum** when it **comes out** the other side of the gas.

5) You see a **continuous spectrum** with **black lines** in it corresponding to the **absorbed wavelengths**.

6) If you **compare** the **absorption** and **emission spectra** of a **particular gas**, the **black lines** in the **absorption spectrum match up** to the **bright lines** in the **emission spectrum**.

white light → cool gas

excited gas

Practice Questions

Q1 Give two different ways to describe the nature of light.
Q2 What is a photon?
Q3 Write down the two formulas you can use to find the energy of a photon. Define all the symbols you use.
Q4 What is an electronvolt? What is 1 eV in joules?
Q5 Describe line absorption and line emission spectra. How are these two types of spectra produced?

Exam Question

Q1 An electron is accelerated through a potential difference of 12.1 V.

a) How much kinetic energy has it gained in i) eV and ii) joules? [2 marks]

b) This electron hits a hydrogen atom in its ground state and excites it.

   i) Explain what is meant by excitation. [1 mark]

   ii) Using the energy values on the right, calculate which energy level the electron from the hydrogen atom is excited to. [1 mark]

   iii) Calculate the energies and frequencies of all the photons that might be emitted as the electron returns to its ground state. [6 marks]

$n = 5$	-0.54 eV
$n = 4$	-0.85 eV
$n = 3$	-1.5 eV
$n = 2$	-3.4 eV
$n = 1$	-13.6 eV

Light can be a particle — well that's a twist in the tale...

Physics is just ridiculous sometimes. But learn it you must — get your head around those energy levels in atoms folks.

The Photoelectric Effect

I think they should rename 'the photoelectric effect' as 'the piece-of-cake effect' — it's not easy, I just like cake.

Shining Light on a Metal can Release Electrons

If you shine **light** of a **high enough frequency** onto the **surface of a metal**, the metal will **emit electrons**. For **most** metals, this **frequency** falls in the **UV** range.

1) **Free electrons** on the **surface** of the metal **absorb energy** from the light.

2) If an electron **absorbs enough** energy, the **bonds** holding it to the metal **break** and the electron is **released**.

3) This is called the **photoelectric effect** and the electrons emitted are called **photoelectrons**.

'Light' means any EM radiation — not just visible light.

ultraviolet radiation

electrons

You don't need to know the details of any experiments on this, you just need to learn the three main conclusions:

Conclusion 1	For a given metal, **no photoelectrons are emitted** if the radiation has a frequency **below** a certain value — called the **threshold frequency**.
Conclusion 2	The photoelectrons are emitted with a variety of kinetic energies ranging from zero to some maximum value. This value of **maximum kinetic energy** increases with the **frequency** of the radiation, and is **unaffected** by the **intensity** of the radiation.
Conclusion 3	The **number** of photoelectrons emitted per second is **proportional** to the **intensity** of the radiation.

These are the two that had scientists puzzled. They can't be explained using wave theory.

Intensity is the power (the energy transferred per second) hitting a given area of the metal (see page 69).

The Photoelectric Effect Couldn't be Explained by Wave Theory...

According to wave theory:

1) For a particular frequency of light, the **energy** carried is **proportional** to the **intensity** of the beam.

2) The energy carried by the light would be **spread evenly** over the wavefront.

3) **Each** free electron on the surface of the metal would gain a **bit of energy** from each incoming wave.

4) Gradually, each electron would gain **enough energy** to leave the metal.

SO... The **higher the intensity** of the wave, the **more energy** it should transfer to each electron — the kinetic energy should increase with intensity. There's **no explanation** for the **kinetic energy** depending only on the **frequency**.

There is also **no explanation** for the **threshold frequency**. According to **wave theory**, the electrons should be emitted **eventually**, no matter what the **frequency** is.

Charlotte thought that landing on her head would get her top marks for beam intensity.

The Photon Model Explained the Photoelectric Effect Nicely

According to the photon model (see page 86):

1) When light hits its surface, the metal is **bombarded** by photons.

2) If one of these photons is **absorbed** by a free electron, the electron will gain energy equal to *hf*.

Before an electron can **leave** the surface of the metal, it needs enough energy to **break the bonds holding it there**. This energy is called the **work function energy** (symbol ϕ, phi) and its **value** depends on the **metal**.

The Photoelectric Effect

The Photon Model Explains the Threshold Frequency...

1) If the energy **gained** by an electron (on the surface of the metal) from a photon is **greater** than the **work function**, the electron is **emitted**.

2) If it **isn't**, the metal will heat up, but **no electrons** will be emitted.

3) Since, for **electrons** to be released, $hf \geq \phi$, the **threshold frequency** must be:

$$f = \frac{\phi}{h}$$

...and the Maximum Kinetic Energy

1) The **energy transferred** to an electron is **hf**.

2) The **kinetic energy** the electron will be carrying when it **leaves** the metal is *hf* **minus** any energy it's **lost** on the way out. Electrons **deeper** down in the metal lose more energy than the electrons on the **surface**, which explains the **range** of energies.

3) The **minimum** amount of energy it can lose is the **work function**, so the **maximum kinetic energy** of a photoelectron, $E_{k\ (max)}$, is *hf* minus the work function, which gives the photoelectric equation:

$$hf = \phi + \frac{1}{2}mv_{max}^2$$

You should recognise this — this part of the equation is just the maximum kinetic energy, $E_{k\ (max)}$.

4) The **kinetic energy** of the electrons is **independent of the intensity** (the **number** of photons **per second** on an **area**), as they can **only absorb one photon** at a time. Increasing the **intensity** just means **more photons per second** on an **area** — each photon has the **same energy** as before.

Practice Questions

Q1 Explain what the photoelectric effect is.

Q2 What three conclusions were drawn from experimentation on the photoelectric effect?

Q3 What is meant by the term threshold frequency?

Q4 Write down the equation that relates the work function of a metal and the threshold frequency.

Q5 Write down an equation that relates the maximum kinetic energy of a photoelectron released from a metal surface and the frequency of the incident light on the surface.

Exam Questions

$h = 6.63 \times 10^{-34}\ Js;\ e = 1.60 \times 10^{-19}\ C$

Q1 The work function of calcium is 2.9 eV. Calculate the threshold frequency of radiation needed for the photoelectric effect to take place. [2 marks]

Q2 The surface of a copper plate is illuminated with monochromatic ultraviolet light, with a frequency of 2.0×10^{15} Hz. The work function for copper is 4.7 eV.

    a) Calculate the energy in eV carried by one photon of the ultraviolet light. [2 marks]

    b) Calculate the maximum kinetic energy of a photoelectron emitted from the copper surface. [2 marks]

Q3 Explain why the photoelectric effect only occurs after the incident light has reached a certain frequency. [2 marks]

I'm so glad we got that all cleared up...

Yep, the photoelectric effect is a bit tricky. The most important bits here are why wave theory doesn't explain the phenomenon, and why the photon theory does. A good way to learn conceptual stuff like this is to try to explain it to someone else. You'll get most formulas in your handy data sheet, but it's probably a good idea to learn them too...

Wave-Particle Duality

Is it a wave? Is it a particle? No, it's a wave. No, it's a particle. No it's not, it's a wave. No don't be daft, it's a particle. (etc.)

There's Evidence for Light Being a **Wave** and for Light Being a **Particle**

Towards the end of the **17th century**, two important **theories of light** were published — one by Isaac Newton and the other by Huygens. Newton's theory suggested that light was made up of tiny particles, which he called **"corpuscles"**, and Huygens put forward a theory using **waves**.

Interference and Diffraction show Light as a Wave

The **corpuscular** theory could explain **reflection** and **refraction**, but **diffraction** and **interference** (p.84-85) are both uniquely wave properties. Over 100 years later, it was shown that light could interfere and diffract, so that settled the argument... for now.

The Photoelectric Effect Shows Light Behaving as a Particle

After another 100 years or so, the debate was raging once again after the photoelectric effect was observed (p.88).

1) **Einstein** explained the results of **photoelectricity experiments** by thinking of the **beam of light** as a series of **particle-like photons** (see p.86). He published his particle theory of light in **1905**.

2) If a **photon** of light is a **discrete** bundle of energy, then it can **interact** with an **electron** in a **one-to-one way**.

3) **All** the **energy** in the **photon** is **given** to one **electron**.

De Broglie Came up With the Wave-Particle Duality Theory

1) In **1924**, Louis de Broglie made a **bold suggestion** in his **PhD thesis**:

> If **'wave-like' light** showed **particle properties** (photons), **'particles'** like **electrons** should be expected to show **wave-like properties**.

2) The **de Broglie equation** relates a **wave property** (**wavelength**, λ) to a **moving particle property** (momentum, p). h = Planck constant = 6.63×10^{-34} Js.

$$\lambda = \frac{h}{p}$$

I'm not impressed — this is just speculation. What do you think Dad?

3) The de Broglie wave of a particle can be interpreted as a **'probability wave'** — the **likelihood** of finding a particle at a point is **directly proportional** to the **square** of the **amplitude** of the wave at that point.

4) Many physicists at the time **weren't very impressed** — his ideas were just **speculation**. But later experiments **confirmed** the wave nature of electrons.

Electron Diffraction shows the Wave Nature of Electrons

1) In **1927**, two American physicists, **Clinton Davisson** and **Lester Germer**, succeeded in diffracting **electrons**.

2) **Diffraction patterns** are observed when **accelerated electrons** in a vacuum tube **interact** with the **spaces** between **carbon atoms** in **polycrystalline graphite**.

3) This **confirms** that electrons show **wave-like** properties.

4) According to wave theory, the **spread** of the **lines** in the diffraction pattern **increases** if the **wavelength** of the wave is **greater**.

5) In electron diffraction experiments, a **smaller accelerating voltage**, i.e. **slower** electrons, gives **widely spaced** rings.

6) **Increase** the **electron speed** and the diffraction pattern circles **squash together** towards the **middle**. This fits in with the **de Broglie** equation above — if the **momentum** is **higher**, the **wavelength** is **shorter** and the **spread** of lines is **smaller**.

7) Electron diffraction was a **huge** discovery — this was the first **direct evidence** for de Broglie's theory.

> In general, λ for **electrons** accelerated in a **vacuum tube** is about the **same size** as electromagnetic waves in the **X-ray** part of the spectrum.

Wave-Particle Duality

Particles Don't show Wave-Like Properties All the Time

1) You **only** get **diffraction** if a particle interacts with an object of about the **same size** as its **de Broglie wavelength**.
2) A **tennis ball**, for example, with **mass 0.058 kg** and **speed 100 ms⁻¹** has a **de Broglie wavelength** of **10⁻³⁴ m**.
That's **10¹⁹ times smaller** than the **nucleus** of an **atom**! There's nothing that small for it to interact with.

Example: An electron of mass 9.11×10^{-31} kg is fired from an electron gun at 7.00×10^6 ms⁻¹. What size object will the electron need to interact with in order to diffract?

Momentum of electron $= p = mv = (9.11 \times 10^{-31}) \times (7.00 \times 10^6) = 6.377 \times 10^{-24}$ kg ms⁻¹

$$\lambda = \frac{h}{p} = \frac{6.63 \times 10^{-34}}{6.377 \times 10^{-24}} = \mathbf{1.04 \times 10^{-10}} \text{ m (to 3 s.f.)}$$

Electrons with a wavelength of around 1×10^{-10} m are **likely** to be diffracted by the atoms in **polycrystalline structures**.

3) A **shorter wavelength** gives **less diffraction effects**. This fact is used in the **electron microscope**.
4) **Diffraction** effects **blur detail** on an image. If you want to **resolve tiny detail** in an **image**, you need a **shorter wavelength**. **Light** blurs out detail more than 'electron-waves' do, so an **electron microscope** can resolve **finer detail** than a **light microscope**. They can let you look at things as tiny as a single strand of DNA... which is nice.

Practice Questions

Q1 Which observations show light to have a 'wave-like' character?
Q2 Which observations show light to have a 'particle' character?
Q3 What happens to the de Broglie wavelength of a particle if its velocity increases?
Q4 Describe the experimental evidence that shows electrons have a 'wave-like' character.

Exam Questions

proton mass, $m_p = 1.673 \times 10^{-27}$ kg; electron mass, $m_e = 9.11 \times 10^{-31}$ kg

Q1 a) State what is meant by the wave-particle duality of electromagnetic radiation. [1 mark]

 b) Calculate the momentum of an electron with a de Broglie wavelength of 590 nm. [2 marks]

Q2 Electrons travelling at a speed of 3.50×10^6 ms⁻¹ exhibit wave properties.

 a) Calculate the wavelength of these electrons. [2 marks]

 b) Calculate the speed of protons which would have the same wavelength as these electrons. [2 marks]

 c) Some electrons and protons were accelerated from rest by the same potential difference, giving them the same kinetic energy. Explain why they will have different wavelengths. [3 marks]

Q3 Electrons are directed at a thin slice of graphite at high speed and a diffraction pattern is observed. Which of the following statements correctly describe a conclusion that this observation supports? [1 mark]

 1 Electrons can show particle-like behaviour.
 2 Waves can show particle-like behaviour.
 3 Photons can show wave-like behaviour.
 4 Electrons can show wave-like behaviour.

 A 1, 2 and 4 B 4 only C 3 only D 1 and 4 only

Don't hide your wave-particles under a bushel...

Right — I think we'll all agree that quantum physics is a wee bit strange when you come to think about it. What it's saying is that electrons and photons aren't really waves, and they aren't really particles — they're both... at the same time. It's what quantum physicists like to call a 'juxtaposition of states'. Well they would, wouldn't they...

Answers

Topic 1 — Working as a Physicist

Page 3 — The Scientific Process

1 **A maximum of two marks can be awarded for structure and reasoning of the written response:**
2 marks:
The answer is coherent and constructed logically, and displays clear reasoning and links between points throughout.
1 mark:
The answer is partially logical, with some reasoning and links between points.
0 marks:
The answer has no structure and no links between points.
Here are some points your answer may include:

* The proposed power station would produce electricity without producing greenhouse gases, and so replacing a nearby coal-fired power station could benefit the environment by helping to limit human contribution to climate change.
* As the proposed power station generates energy renewably, it won't use up resources, which will also benefit the environment.
* However, the power station could have a negative effect on the natural environment in the local area (for example by interfering with local habitats or through pollution during its construction).
* As well as damaging the environment, if the power station spoils the scenic coastline it may be unpopular with local people.
* As the coastline is important for tourism in the area, this could also damage the local economy.
* Building the new power station (and closing down the coal-fired power station) may be expensive.
* If the proposed power station causes a coal-fired power station to close, people there could lose their jobs.
* On the other hand, building a new power station could create other new jobs in the area.
[4 marks — 4 marks if 6 points mentioned including social, environmental, and economic factors, 3 marks if 4-5 points mentioned, covering at least two aspects of the question, 2 marks if 2-3 points mentioned, 1 mark if 1 point mentioned.]

Page 5 — Quantities and Units

1 a) SI base unit of mass = kg.
SI derived unit of volume = [SI base unit of length]^3 = m^3.
$\rho = m / V$, so in SI base units ρ = kg / m^3 = **kg m^{-3} [1 mark]**
b) m = 9.8 g = 9.8 × 10^{-3} kg
V = (11 mm)^3 = (11 × 10^{-3} m)^3 = 1.331 × 10^{-6} m^3 *[1 mark]*
$\rho = m / V$ = (9.8 × 10^{-3}) ÷ (1.331 × 10^{-6})
      = 7362.88... = **7400 kg m^{-3} (to 2 s.f.) [1 mark]**
You could also have worked this out in g mm^{-3} then converted your answer, but this way is much easier.
c) A bath tub is roughly 1.5 m × 0.5 m × 0.5 m = 0.375 m^3 *[1 mark]*
$\rho = m / V$, so $m = \rho V$ = 1000 × 0.375 = 375 kg ≈ **400 kg (to 1 s.f.)**
[1 mark]
If you correctly calculated the mass using a volume between 0.2 m^3 and 0.8 m^3 you can award yourself the marks.

Page 7 — Planning and Implementing

1 a) Independent variable: light level / distance from the light source, dependent variable: resistance of the LDR *[1 mark]*.
b) Any two of: e.g. the light source used / the background lighting in the room / the temperature of the room/LDR/wires / the potential difference / the power supply the LDR is connected to / the length of wires in the circuit / the type of wires in the circuit / the multimeter used to measure the resistance.
[2 marks available — 1 mark for each correct answer.]

Page 9 — Analysing Results

1 a)
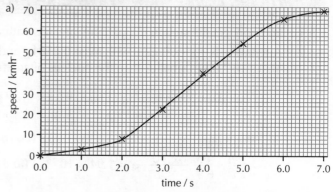

[1 mark for both axes drawn to a sensible scale, 1 mark for labelling both axes correctly, 1 mark for all the points drawn correctly and 1 mark for a sensible line of best fit.]
b) The graph is linear between 2 and 5 seconds *[1 mark]*.
Accept an answer of 6 s as the upper limit if the graph in part a) agrees.
c) The maximum acceleration is the value of the steepest gradient, which is the linear portion of the graph *[1 mark]*:

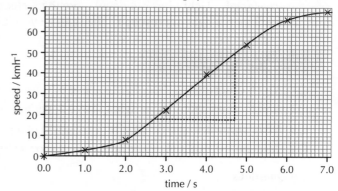

change in speed = 50 − 18 = 32 km hr^{-1} = 32 ÷ (60 × 60)
        = 0.0088... km s^{-1} *[1 mark]*
change in time = 4.7 − 2.7 = 2.0 s *[1 mark]*
acceleration = 0.0088... ÷ 2.0 = 0.0044... km s^{-2}
        = **0.0044 km s^{-2} or 57 000 km hr^{-2} (to 2 s.f.) [1 mark]**
Accept an answer in the range 0.0040-0.0046 km s^{-2} or 54 000-60 000 km hr^{-2}.

Page 11 — Measurements and Uncertainties

1 a) (0.02 ÷ 0.52) × 100 = 3.846... = **4% (to 1 s.f.) [1 mark]**
b) (0.02 ÷ 0.94) × 100 = 2.127... = **2% (to 1 s.f.) [1 mark]**
c) acceleration = change in velocity / time = (0.94 − 0.52) ÷ 2.5
        = 0.168 ms^{-2} *[1 mark]*
Absolute error in change of velocity = 0.02 + 0.02 = 0.04 ms^{-1}
Percentage uncertainty in
change of velocity: (0.04 ÷ (0.94 − 0.52)) × 100 = 9.523...%
[1 mark]
Percentage uncertainty in time taken = (0.5 ÷ 2.5) × 100 = 20%
Percentage uncertainty in acceleration = 9.523...% + 20%
        = 29.523...% *[1 mark]*
Absolute error in acceleration = 0.168 × (29.523... ÷ 100)
        = 0.0496 ms^{-2}
So the acceleration = **0.17 ± 0.05 ms^{-2} (to 2 s.f.) [1 mark]**

Page 13 — Evaluating and Concluding

1 a) t = 0.32 seconds, v = 2.0 ms^{-1} *[1 mark]*
b) E.g. The results do not support this conclusion *[1 mark]*, because the student has only collected data for a small range of times so he cannot draw conclusions about times longer than those he measured *[1 mark]* / because the student has only investigated one object so he cannot draw conclusions about other objects *[1 mark]*.

Answers

Topic 2 — Mechanics

Page 15 — Scalars and Vectors

1

Weight 75 N — Resultant force, F — Wind 20.0 N — θ

$F^2 = 20.0^2 + 75^2 = 6025$
So $F = 78$ N (to 2 s.f.)
$\tan \theta = 20.0 / 75 = 0.266...$
So $\theta = \tan^{-1} 0.266... = 15°$ (to 2 s.f.)
The resultant force on the rock is **78 N (to 2 s.f.) [1 mark]**
at an angle of **15° (to 2 s.f.) [1 mark]** to the vertical.
Make sure you know which angle you're finding — and label it on your diagram.

2 horizontal component, v_h

15° — vertical component, v_v — velocity 20.0 ms⁻¹

horizontal component $v_h = 20.0 \times \cos 15.0°$
  = **19.3 ms⁻¹ (to 3 s.f.) [1 mark]**
vertical component $v_v = 20 \times \sin 15.0°$
  = **5.18 ms⁻¹ (to 3 s.f.) [1 mark]**

3 E.g. current, $v_{river} = 0.20$ ms⁻¹

v_h — 120° — 60.0° — driving velocity, $v_{boat} = 1.54$ ms⁻¹ — R — v_v

horizontal component $v_{river} = 0.20$ ms⁻¹
vertical component $v_{river} = 0$ ms⁻¹
horizontal component $v_{boat} = 1.54 \times \cos 60.0 = 0.77$ ms⁻¹
vertical component $v_{boat} = 1.54 \times \sin 60.0 = 1.333...$ ms⁻¹
So, horizontal $v_{resultant} = 0.20 + 0.77 = 0.97$ ms⁻¹ **[1 mark]**
vertical $v_{resultant} = 0 + 1.333... = 1.333...$ ms⁻¹ **[1 mark]**
Combine the vertical and horizontal components of R.

$v_h = 0.97$ ms⁻¹ — θ — R — $v_v = 1.333...$ ms⁻¹

$v_{resultant} = \sqrt{0.97^2 + 1.333...^2} = 1.649...$ ms⁻¹
  = **1.6 ms⁻¹ (to 2 s.f.) [1 mark]**

$\tan \theta = 1.333... \div 0.97 = \tan^{-1} 1.374...$ so $\theta = $ **54° (to 2 s.f.)**
So the resultant velocity of the boat is 1.6 ms⁻¹ at an angle of 54°
to the current **[1 mark]**.

Page 17 — Motion with Uniform Acceleration

1 a) $a = -9.81$ ms⁻², $t = 5.0$ s, $u = 0$ ms⁻¹, $v = ?$
  use : $v = u + at$
    $v = 0 + 5.0 \times -9.81$ **[1 mark]**
    $v = -49.05 = $ **−49 ms⁻¹ (to 2 s.f.) [1 mark]**.
  NB: It's negative because she's falling downwards and we took upwards as the positive direction.
  b) Use: $s = \dfrac{(u+v)t}{2}$ or $s = ut + \frac{1}{2}at^2$
    $s = \dfrac{-49.05 \times 5.0}{2}$ $s = 0 + \frac{1}{2} \times -9.81 \times 5.0^2$ **[1 mark]**
    $s = -122.625$ m $s = -122.625$ m
  So she falls **120 m (to 2 s.f.) [1 mark]**

2 a) $v = 0$ ms⁻¹, $t = 3.2$ s, $s = 40$ m, $u = ?$
  use: $s = \left(\dfrac{u+v}{2}\right)t$
    $40 = 3.2u \div 2$ **[1 mark]**
    $u = 80 \div 3.2 = $ **25 ms⁻¹ [1 mark]**
  b) Use: $v^2 = u^2 + 2as$
    $0 = 25^2 + 80a$ **[1 mark]**
    $-80a = 625$
    $a = -7.81... = $ **−7.8 ms⁻² (to 2 s.f.) [1 mark]**
  You could also have solved this using $v = u + at$.

3 a) Take upstream as negative: $v = 5$ ms⁻¹, $a = 6$ ms⁻², $s = 1.2$ m, $u = ?$
  use: $v^2 = u^2 + 2as$
    $5^2 = u^2 + 2 \times 6 \times 1.2$ **[1 mark]**
    $u^2 = 25 - 14.4 = 10.6$
    $u = -3.255... = $ **−3 ms⁻¹ (to 1 s.f.) [1 mark]**
  The negative root is taken because the boat is pushed upstream at the start, which we've taken to be the negative direction.
  b) From furthest point: $u = 0$ ms⁻¹, $a = 6$ ms⁻², $v = 5$ ms⁻¹, $s = ?$
    use: $v^2 = u^2 + 2as$ **[1 mark]**
    $5^2 = 0 + 2 \times 6 \times s$
    $s = 25 \div 12 = 2.083... = $ **2 m (to 1 s.f.) [1 mark]**

Page 19 — Free Fall

1 a) The student needs the computer to record:
  The time for the first strip of card to pass through the beam **[1 mark]**
  The time for the second strip of card to pass through the beam **[1 mark]**
  The time between these events **[1 mark]**.
  b) Average speed of first strip while it breaks the light beam =
      width of strip ÷ time to pass through beam **[1 mark]**
  Average speed of second strip while it breaks the light beam =
      width of strip ÷ time to pass through beam **[1 mark]**
  Acceleration = (second speed – first speed)
      ÷ time between light beam being broken **[1 mark]**
  c) E.g. the device will accelerate while the beam is broken by the strips **[1 mark]** / The device will experience air resistance, which will slow it down **[1 mark]**.

2 a) You know $s = 5.0$ m, $a = -g$, $v = 0$
  You need to find u, so use $v^2 = u^2 + 2as$
    $0 = u^2 - 2 \times 9.81 \times 5.0$ **[1 mark]**
    $u^2 = 98.1$, so $u = 9.90... = $ **9.9 ms⁻¹ (to 2 s.f.) [1 mark]**
  b) You know $a = -g$, $v = 0$ at highest point, $u = 9.90...$ ms⁻¹
  You need to find t, so use $v = u + at$
    $0 = 9.90... - 9.81t$ **[1 mark]**
    $t = 9.90.../9.81 = $ **1.0 s (to 2 s.f.) [1 mark]**
  c) Her velocity as she lands back on the trampoline will be **−9.9 ms⁻¹ (to 2 s.f.). [1 mark]**
  She has a negative velocity because she's moving downwards and the same magnitude as her initial speed because no energy has been lost due to air resistance.

Answers

Page 21 — Projectile Motion

1 a) You only need to worry about the vertical motion of the stone.
$u = 0$ ms^{-1}, $s = -560$ m, $a = -g = -9.81$ ms^{-2}, $t = ?$
You need to find t, so use: $s = ut + \frac{1}{2}at^2$
$-560 = 0 + \frac{1}{2} \times -9.81 \times t^2$
$t = \sqrt{\dfrac{2 \times (-560)}{-9.81}}$ *[1 mark]*
$t = 10.68... = $ **11 s (to 2 s.f.)** *[1 mark]*

b) You know that in the horizontal direction:
$v = 20$ m/s, $t = 10.68...$ s, $a = 0$, $s = ?$
$s = v \times t = 20 \times 10.68...$ *[1 mark]*
$s = 213.69... = $ **210 m (to 2 s.f.)** *[1 mark]*

2 C *[1 mark]*
Use $v^2 = u^2 + 2as$ to find the vertical displacement when $v = 0$. The arrow was fired from 1.0 m above the ground so don't forget to include the extra metre in your calculations.

Page 23 — Displacement-Time Graphs

1 Split graph into four sections:

A: acceleration *[1 mark]*
B: constant velocity *[1 mark]*
C: stationary *[1 mark]*
D: constant velocity in opposite direction to A and B *[1 mark]*

2 a)

[4 marks — 1 mark for each section correctly drawn]

b) At A: $v = s \div t = 5 \div 8 = 0.625 = $ **0.6 ms^{-1} (to 1 s.f.)**
At B: $v = $ **0 ms^{-1}**
At C: $v = 3 \div 5 = $ **0.6 ms^{-1}**
At D: $v = -8 \div 10 = $ **−0.8 ms^{-1}**
[2 marks for all correct or just 1 mark for 2 or 3 correct]

Page 25 — Velocity-Time and Acceleration-Time Graphs

1 a)

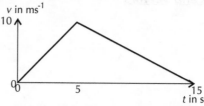

[1 mark for drawing a correctly labelled pair of axes, with a straight line between $v = 0$ ms^{-1}, $t = 0$ s and $v = 10$ ms^{-1}, $t = 5$ s. 1 mark for correctly drawing a straight line between $v = 10$ ms^{-1}, $t = 5$ s and $v = 0$ ms^{-1}, $t = 15$ s.]

[1 mark for drawing a correctly labelled pair of axes, with a straight line between $a = 2$ ms^{-2}, $t = 0$ s and $a = 2$ ms^{-2}, $t = 5$ s. 1 mark for correctly drawing a straight line from $a = 2$ ms^{-2}, $t = 5$ s and $a = -1$ ms^{-2}, $t = 5$ s, and a straight line between $a = -1$ ms^{-2}, $t = 5$ s and $a = -1$ ms^{-2}, $t = 15$ s.]

b) Distance travelled is equal to the area under v-t graph between $t = 0$ and $t = 5$ *[1 mark]* $= 0.5 \times 5 \times 10 = $ **25 m** *[1 mark]*

Page 27 — Forces

1

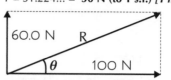

The picture is in equilibrium, so the forces are balanced.
Resolving vertically:
Weight = vertical component of tension × 2
$8 \times 9.81 = 2T \sin 50°$ *[1 mark]*
$78.48 = 0.7660... \times 2T$
$102.448... = 2T$
$T = 51.224... = $ **50 N (to 1 s.f.)** *[1 mark]*

2

By Pythagoras:
$R = \sqrt{100^2 + 60.0^2} = 116.619... = $ **117 N (to 3 s.f.)** *[1 mark]*
$\tan \theta = (60.0 \div 100)$
so $\theta = \tan^{-1} 0.6 = 30.96... = $ **31.0° (to 3 s.f.)** *[1 mark]*

Answers

Page 29 — Newton's Laws of Motion

1 a) Force perpendicular to river flow = 500 − 100 = 400 N *[1 mark]*
Force parallel to river flow = 300 N
Resultant force = $\sqrt{400^2 + 300^2}$ = **500 N** *[1 mark]*
b) $\Sigma F = ma$ so $a = \Sigma F \div m = 500 \div 250 = $ **2 ms⁻²** *[1 mark]*

2 **B** *[1 mark]*
The overall acceleration is a, so ma must be equal to the resultant force, which is the force John is pushing with minus the resistance caused by friction. So $F_{John} - F = ma$, and $F_{John} = ma + F$.

3 The only force acting on each of them is their weight = mg *[1 mark]*. Since $\Sigma F = ma$, this gives $ma = mg$, or $a = g$ *[1 mark]*. Their acceleration doesn't depend on their mass — it's the same for both of them — so they reach the water at the same time *[1 mark]*.

Page 31 — Drag and Terminal Velocity

1 a) The velocity increases at a steady rate, which means the acceleration is constant *[1 mark]*.
Constant acceleration means there must be no atmospheric resistance (atmospheric resistance would increase with velocity, leading to a decrease in acceleration). So there must be no atmosphere *[1 mark]*.
b) velocity

[2 marks — 1 mark for drawing a graph that still starts from the origin, 1 mark for showing the graph curving to show the velocity increasing at a decreasing rate until the velocity is constant.]
Your graph must be a smooth curve which levels out. It must NOT go down at the end.
c) The graph becomes less steep because the acceleration is decreasing *[1 mark]* and because air resistance increases with speed *[1 mark]*. The graph levels out because air resistance has become equal to weight *[1 mark]*.
If the question says 'explain', you won't get marks for just describing what the graph shows — you have to say <u>why</u> it is that shape.

Page 33 — Momentum

1 a) total momentum before collision = total momentum after *[1 mark]*
$(0.60 \times 5.0) + 0 = (0.60 \times -2.4) + 2.0v$
$3 + 1.44 = 2v$ *[1 mark]*
So $v = 2.22 = $ **2.2 ms⁻¹ (to 2 s.f.)** *[1 mark]*
b) $F = \dfrac{\Delta(mv)}{\Delta t} = \dfrac{(0.60 \times 5.0) - (0.60 \times 2.4)}{0.0055}$ *[1 mark]*
= 807.27... = **800 N (to 2 s.f.)** *[1 mark]*

2 momentum before = momentum after *[1 mark]*
$(0.7 \times 0.3) + 0 = 1.1v \Rightarrow 0.21 = 1.1v$ *[1 mark]*
So: $v = 0.190... = $ **0.2 ms⁻¹ (to 1 s.f.)** *[1 mark]*

Page 35 — Work and Power

1 a)

100 cos 40° N
40°
100 N

Force in direction of travel = 100 cos40° = 76.6... N *[1 mark]*
$\Delta W = F\Delta s = 76.6... \times 1500 = 114\,906...$
= **100 000 J (to 1 s.f.)** *[1 mark]*
b) Use the equation for power:
$P = \dfrac{W}{t} = \dfrac{114\,906...}{31 \times 60}$ *[1 mark]*
= 61.77... = **60 W (to 1 s.f.)** *[1 mark]*

Page 35 continued

2 a) Use $\Delta W = F\Delta s$
$\Delta W = 20.0 \times 9.81 \times 3.0$ *[1 mark]* = 588.6
= **590 J (to 2 s.f.)** *[1 mark]*
Remember that 20.0 kg is not the force — it's the mass. So you need to multiply it by 9.81 Nkg⁻¹ to get the weight.
b) First find the time taken to lift the load 3.0 m:
Use $v = \dfrac{\Delta s}{t}$ and rearrange for time:
$t = \dfrac{\Delta s}{v} = \dfrac{3.0}{0.25} = 12$ s *[1 mark]*
Substitute this into the equation for power:
$P = \dfrac{W}{t} = \dfrac{588.6}{12}$ *[1 mark]* = 49.05 = **49 W (to 2 s.f.)** *[1 mark]*

Page 37 — Conservation of Energy and Efficiency

1 a) Use $E_k = \frac{1}{2}mv^2$ and $\Delta E_{grav} = mg\Delta h$ *[1 mark]*
$\frac{1}{2}mv^2 = mg\Delta h$
$\frac{1}{2}v^2 = g\Delta h$
$v^2 = 2g\Delta h = 2 \times 9.81 \times 2.0 = 39.24$ *[1 mark]*
$v = \sqrt{39.24} = 6.264... = $ **6.3 ms⁻¹ (to 2 s.f.)** *[1 mark]*
'Negligible friction' allows you to assume that the changes in kinetic and potential energy will be the same.
b) 2.0 m — no friction means the kinetic energy will all change back into potential energy, so he will rise back up to the same height as he started *[1 mark]*.
c) Put in some more energy by actively 'skating' / 'pumping the board' *[1 mark]*.

2 a) If there's no air resistance, $E_k = \Delta E_{grav} = mg\Delta h$ *[1 mark]*
$E_k = 0.020 \times 9.81 \times 8.0 = 1.5696 = $ **1.6 J (to 2 s.f.)** *[1 mark]*
b) If the ball rebounds to 6.5 m, it has gained gravitational potential energy:
$\Delta E_{grav} = mg\Delta h = 0.020 \times 9.81 \times 6.5 = 1.2753$ J *[1 mark]*
So $1.5696 - 1.2753 = 0.2943 = $ **0.29 J (to 2 s.f.)** is converted to other forms *[1 mark]*.
You could also work out the loss of E_p from the difference in height —
$E_p = 0.020 \times 9.81 \times (8.0 - 6.5) = 0.29$ J (to 2 s.f.).

3 Use efficiency = $\dfrac{\text{useful output energy}}{\text{total input energy}}$
= $(140 - 65) \div 140 = 0.535... = $ **0.54 (to 2 s.f.)** *[1 mark]*

Page 39 — Mass, Weight and Centre of Gravity

1 **B** *[1 mark]*
$W = mg$, so $m = W/g = X/g$.
2 a) Hang the object freely from a point so that it hangs vertically. Hang a plumb bob from the same point, and use it to draw a vertical line down the object *[1 mark]*. Repeat for a different point and find the point of intersection *[1 mark]*. The centre of gravity is halfway through the thickness of the object (by symmetry) at the point of intersection *[1 mark]*.
b) E.g. Source: the object and/or plumb line might move slightly while you're drawing the vertical line *[1 mark]*.
Reduced by: hang the object from a third point to confirm the position of the point of intersection *[1 mark]*.

Page 41 — Moments

1 Moment = force × distance
$60 = 0.40F$ *[1 mark]*, so $F = $ **150 N** *[1 mark]*

2 Clockwise moment = anticlockwise moment
$W \times 2.0 = T \times 0.3$
[1 mark for either line of working]
$60 \times 9.81 \times 2.0 = T \times 0.3$
$T = 3924 = $ **4000 N (to 1 s.f.)** *[1 mark]*
The moments caused by the tension in the spring and the force exerted by the diver on the spring are equal and opposite.

0.3 m
2.0 m
T
$W = mg$

Answers

Topic 3 — Electric Circuits

Page 43 — Charge, Current and Potential Difference

1. Time in seconds = $10 \times 60 = 600$ s
$I = \Delta Q / \Delta t = 4500 / 600 = 7.5 = \textbf{8 A}$ (to 1 s.f.) *[1 mark]*

2. Energy transferred to water = 0.88 × electrical energy input
so the energy input will be 308 / 0.88 = 350 J *[1 mark]*
$V = W/Q$ so $Q = W / V$
$Q = 350 \div 230 = 1.521... = \textbf{1.5 C}$ (to 2 s.f.) *[1 mark]*
The heat energy that the kettle transfers to the water is less than the electrical energy input because the kettle is less than 100% efficient.

3. $I = nqvA$ so $v = I / nqA$
so $v = 13 \div ((5.0 \times 10^{-6}) \times (1.0 \times 10^{29}) \times (1.60 \times 10^{-19}))$ *[1 mark]*
$= 1.625 \times 10^{-4} = \textbf{1.6} \times \textbf{10}^{-4} \textbf{ ms}^{-1}$ **(to 2 s.f.)** *[1 mark]*

Page 45 — Resistance and Resistivity

1. Area $= \pi r^2 = \pi(d/2)^2$ and $d = 1.0 \times 10^{-3}$ m
so area $= \pi \times (0.5 \times 10^{-3})^2 = 7.853... \times 10^{-7}$ m^2 *[1 mark]*
$R = \rho L / A = (2.8 \times 10^{-8} \times 4.0) \div 7.853... \times 10^{-7}$ *[1 mark]*
$= 0.1426... = \textbf{0.14 } \Omega$ (to 2 s.f.) *[1 mark]*

2. a) $R = V / I = 7.00 \div (9.33 \times 10^{-3}) = 750.267...$
$= \textbf{750 } \Omega$ **(to 3 s.f.)** *[1 mark]*
   b) For $V = 3.00$ V, $R = 3.00 \div (4.00 \times 10^{-3}) = 750\ \Omega$
for $V = 11.00$ V, $R = 11.00 \div (14.67 \times 10^{-3}) = 749.82...\ \Omega$ *[1 mark]*
The component is an ohmic conductor (for the range considered) *[1 mark]*, because there is no significant change in resistance for different potential differences *[1 mark]*.

Page 47 — I-V Characteristics

1. a)

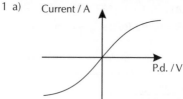

Current / A

P.d. / V

[1 mark]

   b) E.g. Increasing the voltage increases the current, which increases the temperature of the filament bulb *[1 mark]*. This causes the ion lattice in the wire filament to vibrate more, causing the charge carrying electrons to collide with it more frequently, reducing their kinetic energy and thus their mean drift velocity *[1 mark]*. As current is proportional to mean drift velocity *[1 mark]*, this reduces the current for a given potential difference, thus increases the filament bulb's resistance *[1 mark]*.
   c) A temperature increase releases more charge carriers as more electrons have energy to escape their atoms *[1 mark]*. An increase in charge carriers means the current will also increase $(I = nqvA)$ *[1 mark]*. As a result, the resistance will decrease (because $R = V/I$) *[1 mark]*.
   Remember, even though increasing the temperature increases the vibrations of the lattice making it harder for the current to flow, this effect is dwarfed by the release of more charge carriers.

Page 49 — Electrical Energy and Power

1. a) $I = P / V = 920 \div 230 = \textbf{4.0 A}$ *[1 mark]*
   b) $I = V / R = 230 \div 190 = 1.210... = \textbf{1.2 A}$ (to 2 s.f.) *[1 mark]*
   c) $P_{motor} = VI = 230 \times 1.210... = 278.421...$ W *[1 mark]*
   Total power = motor power + heater power
$= 278.421... + 920 = 1198.421...$ W $= \textbf{1.2 kW}$ **(to 2 s.f.)** *[1 mark]*
   You could also answer this question by calculating using
$P_{total} = V_{total}I_{total}$ where $V_{total} = 230$ V (the source p.d.) and $I_{total} = 4.00 + 1.210...$ A.

2. a) Energy transferred = $W = VIt = 12 \times 48 \times 2.0$
$= 1152 = \textbf{1200 J}$ **(to 2 s.f.)** *[1 mark]*
   b) Energy wasted in wires = $W = I^2Rt = 48^2 \times 0.010 \times 2.0 = 46.08$
$= \textbf{46 J}$ **(to 2 s.f.)** *[1 mark]*

Page 51 — E.m.f. and Internal Resistance

1. a) $\varepsilon = I(R + r)$ so $I = \varepsilon / (R + r)$
$= 24 / (4.0 + 0.8) = \textbf{5 A}$ *[1 mark]*
   b) $V = IR = 5 \times 4.0 = \textbf{20 V}$ *[1 mark]*
   You could also have used $\varepsilon = V + Ir$.

2. **C** *[1 mark]*
$\varepsilon = I(R + r)$, but since there are two cells in series replace r with $2r$, and ε with 2ε, then rearrange to find I.

Page 53 — Conservation of Charge & Energy in Circuits

1. a) Resistance of parallel resistors:
$1/R_{parallel} = 1/6.0 + 1/3.0 = 1/2$
$R_{parallel} = 2.0\ \Omega$ *[1 mark]*
   Total resistance:
$R_{total} = 4.0 + R_{parallel} = 4.0 + 2.0 = \textbf{6.0 } \Omega$ *[1 mark]*
   b) $V = I_3 R_{total}$ so rearranging $I_3 = V / R_{total} = 12 / 6.0$
$= \textbf{2.0 A}$ *[1 mark]*
   c) $V = IR = 2.0 \times 4.0 = \textbf{8.0 V}$ *[1 mark]*
   d) E.m.f. = sum of p.d.s in circuit, so $12 = 8.0 + V_{parallel}$
$V_{parallel} = 12 - 8.0 = \textbf{4.0 V}$ *[1 mark]*
   e) $I = V/R$, so
$I_1 = 4.0 / 3.0 = \textbf{1.3 A}$ (to 2 s.f.) *[1 mark]*
$I_2 = 4.0 / 6.0 = \textbf{0.67 A}$ (to 2 s.f.) *[1 mark]*
   You can check your answers by making sure that $I_3 = I_2 + I_1$.

Page 55 — The Potential Divider

1. Parallel circuit, so p.d. across both sets of resistors is 12 V.
   a) There are two equal resistors in the top branch of the circuit. The p.d. between points A and B is equal to the potential difference across one of these resistors:
$V_{AB} = \frac{1}{2} \times 12 = \textbf{6.0 V}$ *[1 mark]*
   b) There are three equal resistors in the bottom branch of the circuit. The p.d. between points A and C is equal to the potential difference across two of them:
$V_{AC} = \frac{2}{3} \times 12 = \textbf{8.0 V}$ *[1 mark]*
   c) $V_{BC} = V_{AC} - V_{AB} = 8 - 6 = \textbf{2.0 V}$ *[1 mark]*

2. a) $V_{AB} = 50/80 \times 12 = \textbf{7.5 V}$ *[1 mark]*
   (ignore the 10 Ω — no current flows that way)
   b) Total resistance of the parallel circuit:
$1/R_T = 1/50 + 1/(10 + 40.0) = 1/25 \Rightarrow R_T = \textbf{25 } \Omega$ *[1 mark]*
   p.d. over the whole parallel arrangement = $25/55 \times 12 = 5.45...$ V *[1 mark]*
   p.d. across AB = $40.0/50 \times 5.45...$
$= 4.36... $ V $= \textbf{4.4 V}$ **(to 2 s.f.)** *[1 mark]*
   current through 40.0 Ω resistor = V/R
$= 4.36.../40.0 = \textbf{0.11 A}$ **(to 2 s.f.)** *[1 mark]*

Topic 4— Materials

Page 57 — Hooke's Law

1. a) Force is proportional to extension. The force is 1.5 times as great, so the new extension will also be 1.5 times the original extension.
new extension = 1.5×4.0 mm = $\textbf{6.0 mm}$ *[1 mark]*
   b) $\Delta F = k\Delta x$ and so $k = \Delta F/\Delta x$
$k = 10.0 \div (4.0 \times 10^{-3}) = \textbf{2500 Nm}^{-1}$ or $\textbf{2.5 Nmm}^{-1}$ *[1 mark]*
   c) Any one from e.g. the string now stretches much further for small increases in force *[1 mark]*. / When the string is loosened it is longer than at the start *[1 mark]*.

2. The rubber band does not obey Hooke's law *[1 mark]* because when the force is doubled from 2.5 N to 5.0 N, the extension increases by a factor of 2.3. *[1 mark]*.
Or you could show that k is different for 2.5 N and 5.0 N.

Answers

Page 59 — Stress, Strain and Elastic Strain Energy

1 a) Area = πr^2 or $\pi\left(\dfrac{d}{2}\right)^2$

So area = $\pi \times \dfrac{(1.0\times10^{-3})^2}{4} = 7.853... \times 10^{-7}$ **[1 mark]**

Stress, $\sigma = \dfrac{F}{A} = 300 \div (7.853... \times 10^{-7}) = 3.819... \times 10^{8}$

= **3.8×10^8 Nm^{-2} (or Pa) (to 2 s.f.) [1 mark]**

b) Strain, $\varepsilon = \dfrac{\Delta x}{x}$

= $(4.0 \times 10^{-3}) \div 2.00 = \mathbf{2.0 \times 10^{-3}}$ **[1 mark]**

2 a) $\Delta F = k\Delta x$ and so rearranging $k = \Delta F \div \Delta x$ **[1 mark]**

$k = 50.0 \div (3.0 \times 10^{-3}) = 1.666... \times 10^{4}$

= **1.7×10^4 Nm^{-1} (to 2 s.f.) [1 mark]**

b) Elastic strain energy, $\Delta E_{el} = \frac{1}{2}F\Delta x$

= $\frac{1}{2} \times 50.0 \times (3.0 \times 10^{-3})$

= **7.5×10^{-2} J [1 mark]**

You could also use $\Delta E_{el} = \frac{1}{2}k\Delta x^2$ and substitute in your value of k.

3

Divide the graph into shapes, then find the area of each:

Area A = $0.5 \times$ base $\times$ height = $0.5 \times 0.2 \times 4 = 0.4$ J

Area B = $0.5 \times (a + b) \times h = 0.5 \times (4 + 6) \times 0.2 = 1$ J

[1 mark for sensibly splitting the area under the graph up and correctly calculating at least one of these areas]

Total elastic strain energy stored = 0.4 + 1

= **1.4 J [1 mark]**

Shape B is a trapezium. The area of a trapezium is given by $A = \frac{1}{2}(a + b) \times h$, where a is the length of the first side, b is the length of the second side and h is the width of the strip. You won't be given this formula in your exam, so if you get stuck you can always break the trapeziums up into rectangles and triangles.

You could also calculate this area by estimating the number of grid squares the area under the graph covers. The area of each grid square is equal to $2 \times 0.1 = 0.2$ J. There are approximately 7 grid squares under the graph, so the total energy stored is approximately $7 \times 0.2 = 1.4$ J.

4 The force needed to compress the spring is:

$\Delta F = k\Delta x = 40.8 \times 0.05 = 2.04$ N **[1 mark]**

The elastic strain energy in the spring is then:

$E = \frac{1}{2}F\Delta x = \frac{1}{2} \times 2.04 \times 0.05 = 0.051$ J **[1 mark]**

Assume all this energy is converted to kinetic energy in the ball.

$E = E_{kinetic} = \mathbf{0.051}$ **J [1 mark]**.

You could also begin by using Hooke's law to replace F in the formula for elastic strain energy, to give $\Delta E_{el} = \frac{1}{2}k\Delta x^2$, and then substituting into this.

Page 61 — The Young Modulus

1 Cross-sectional area = πr^2 or $\pi\left(\dfrac{d}{2}\right)^2$

So area = $\pi \times \dfrac{(0.60\times10^{-3})^2}{4} = 2.827... \times 10^{-7}$ m^2 **[1 mark]**

Stress, $\sigma = \dfrac{F}{A} = 80.0 \div (2.827... \times 10^{-7})$

= $2.829... \times 10^{8}$ Nm^{-2} **[1 mark]**

Strain, $\varepsilon = \dfrac{\Delta x}{x} = (3.6 \times 10^{-3}) \div 2.50$

= 1.44×10^{-3} **[1 mark]**

Young modulus, $E = \dfrac{\sigma}{\varepsilon} = (2.829... \times 10^{8}) \div (1.44 \times 10^{-3})$

= $1.964... \times 10^{11}$

= **2.0×10^{11} Nm^{-2} (to 2 s.f.) [1 mark]**

2 $E = \dfrac{\sigma}{\varepsilon} = \dfrac{F}{A} \div \dfrac{\Delta x}{x} = \dfrac{Fx}{\Delta x A}$. Force, original length and extension are the same for both wires, so $E \propto \dfrac{1}{A}$.

The wire B has half the cross-sectional area of the wire A. So the Young modulus of wire B (E_B) must be twice that of the wire A *[1 mark]*.

$E_B = 2 \times (7.0 \times 10^{10}) = \mathbf{1.4 \times 10^{11}}$ **Nm^{-2} [1 mark]**

3 a) Young modulus, $E = \dfrac{\sigma}{\varepsilon}$

$\varepsilon = \dfrac{\sigma}{E} = (2.6 \times 10^{8}) \div (1.3 \times 10^{11})$ *[1 mark]*

= **2.0×10^{-3} [1 mark]**

b) $\sigma = \dfrac{F}{A}$ and so $A = \dfrac{F}{\sigma} = 100 \div (2.6 \times 10^{8})$ *[1 mark]*

= $3.846... \times 10^{-7}$

= **3.8×10^{-7} m^2 (to 2 s.f.) [1 mark]**

c) Strain energy per unit volume

= $\frac{1}{2} \times \sigma \times \varepsilon = \frac{1}{2} \times (2.6 \times 10^{8}) \times (2.0 \times 10^{-3})$ *[1 mark]*

= **2.6×10^{5} Jm^{-3} [1 mark]**

Give the mark if answer is consistent with the value calculated for strain in part a).

Page 63 — Stress-Strain and Force-Extension Graphs

1 E.g.

[1 mark for a stiff and weak curve that stops at a low stress and a low strain. 1 mark for a strong and less stiff curve that stops at a high stress and a high strain]

2 a) Yield stress = 900 MNm^{-2} *[1 mark]*

b) Energy per unit volume = area under the graph

Limit of proportionality = 800 MNm^{-2} *[1 mark]*

= $(800 \times 0.2) \div 2 = \mathbf{80}$ **MJm^{-3} (or 8×10^{7} J m^{-3}) [1 mark]**

Page 65 — Density, Upthrust and Viscosity

1 a) Stokes's law gives viscous drag, $F = 6\pi\eta r v$, where η is the viscosity of the fluid (Nsm^{-2} or Pas), r is the radius of the object (m) and v is the speed the object is moving at (ms^{-1}) *[1 mark]*.

b) Any three of: The object moving through the fluid must be small *[1 mark]* / spherical *[1 mark]* / moving through the fluid with laminar flow *[1 mark]* / moving slowly through the fluid *[1 mark]*.

c) Weight – drag – upthrust = 0 *[1 mark]*

So you can work out the weight by calculating the drag and upthrust acting on the ball bearing.

Upthrust = weight of fluid displaced = $m_{liquid} \times g$

$m_{liquid} = \rho_{liquid} \times V_{liquid}$

= $1400 \times \frac{4}{3}\pi(3.0 \times 10^{-3})^3 = 1.583... \times 10^{-4}$ kg *[1 mark]*

So upthrust = $m_{liquid} \times g = 1.583... \times 10^{-4} \times 9.81$

= $1.553... \times 10^{-3}$ N *[1 mark]*

Drag = $F = 6\pi\eta r v = 6\pi \times 3.0 \times (3.0 \times 10^{-3}) \times 0.040$

= $6.785... \times 10^{-3}$... N *[1 mark]*

So weight = $(1.553... \times 10^{-3}) + (6.785... \times 10^{-3}) = 8.339... \times 10^{-3}$

= **8.4×10^{-3} N (to 2 s.f.) [1 mark]**

Answers

Topic 5 — Waves and Particle Nature of Light

Page 67— The Nature of Waves

1 a) The gain is set to 2.0 volts/div and the trace
   has a maximum amplitude of 2 divisions.
   So, the maximum voltage = 2 × 2.0 = **4.0 V** *[1 mark]*
   b) One cycle spans 3 divisions, so
   $T = 3 \times 3.0$ ms = 9.0 ms = 9.0×10^{-3} s *[1 mark]*
   $f = 1/T = 1/9.0 \times 10^{-3}$ *[1 mark]*
   $f = 111.1... = $ **110 Hz (to 2 s.f.)** *[1 mark]*
   $v = f\lambda$ so $\lambda = v/f$
   $\lambda = 280/111.1...$ *[1 mark]*
   $\lambda = 2.52$ m = **2.5 m (to 2 s.f.)** *[1 mark]*

Page 69 — Types of Wave

1 a) $I = P \div A = 10.0 \div 0.002 = $ **5000 Wm^{-2}** *[1 mark]*
   b) D *[1 mark]*

Page 71 — Polarisation of Waves

1 a) They are at right angles to one another (90°, 270° etc.) *[1 mark]*.
   b) It would be half of the intensity of the original light *[1 mark]*.
   This is because at 45° the vertical and horizontal contributions are equal, so
   the intensity is halved between them.

Page 73 — Ultrasound Imaging

1   E.g. A transducer is used to send pulses of ultrasound waves
   into the patient's body *[1 mark]*. Waves are partially reflected
   and partially transmitted when they meet an interface, with the
   proportion reflected increasing with the difference in density
   between the media *[1 mark]*. A gel is put on the patient's
   skin with a similar density to tissue, to increase the amount of
   ultrasound transmitted into the patient's body *[1 mark]*. When
   the ultrasound waves meet an interface in the patient's body, for
   example between different tissues, some of the ultrasound waves
   are reflected back, which are then detected by the transducer
   [1 mark]. From the time taken for the signals to return, a
   computer attached to the transducer can work out the location of
   different tissue boundaries, and build up an image of inside the
   patient's body *[1 mark]*.

2 a) Sound waves with short wavelengths diffract less than sounds
   waves with long wavelengths *[1 mark]*. So decreasing the
   wavelength means that the waves spread out less, which improves
   the precision of the location of tissue surfaces *[1 mark]*. This
   means the image produced is of a higher quality *[1 mark]*.
   b) The shorter the pulse length, the less likely it is that a reflected
   ultrasound wave will reach the transducer whilst it is still
   transmitting the pulse *[1 mark]*. The transducer cannot receive the
   reflected waves whilst it is transmitting, so if this did happen, data
   would be lost *[1 mark]*. A longer time between the pulses means
   a reflected ultrasound wave is less likely to reach the transducer
   after it has transmitted the next pulse *[1 mark]*. If this did happen,
   the computer would not be able to distinguish which transmitted
   wave corresponded with which reflected wave, and so image
   quality would be lost *[1 mark]*.

Page 75 — Superposition and Coherence

1 a) The frequencies and wavelengths of the two sources must be
   equal *[1 mark]* and the phase difference must be constant
   [1 mark].
   b) Interference will only be noticeable if the amplitudes of the two
   waves are approximately equal *[1 mark]*.

2 B *[1 mark]*

Page 77 — Stationary (Standing) Waves

1   Rearrange $v = \sqrt{\frac{T}{\mu}}$ for μ:
   $\mu = \frac{T}{v^2} = \frac{3.2}{16^2} = 0.0125$ kgm^{-1} *[1 mark]*
   $\mu = \frac{M}{l}$, so $M = \mu l = 0.0125 \times 2.8 = $ **0.035 kg** (= 35 g) *[1 mark]*

2 a) The length of the string for a stationary wave oscillating at its first
   harmonic frequency is half the wavelength of the wave *[1 mark]*,
   so $\lambda = 2 \times 1.2 = $ **2.4 m** *[1 mark]*.
   b) $f_{new} = \frac{1}{2l}\sqrt{\frac{2T}{\mu}} = \sqrt{2} \times \left(\frac{1}{2l}\sqrt{\frac{T}{\mu}}\right) = \sqrt{2} \times f_{original}$ *[1 mark]*
   $f_{new} = \sqrt{2} \times 10$ *[1 mark]* = 14.142...
   = **14 Hz (to 2 s.f.)** *[1 mark]*
   c) When the string forms a standing wave, its amplitude varies from
   a maximum at the antinodes to zero at the nodes *[1 mark]*. In
   a progressive wave all the points vibrate at the same amplitude
   [1 mark].

Page 79 — Refractive Index

1 a) $n_{diamond} = c/v = (3.00 \times 10^8)/(1.24 \times 10^8) = 2.419...$
   = **2.42 (to 3 s.f.)** *[1 mark]*
   b) $n_{air}\sin\theta_1 = n_{diamond}\sin\theta_2$, $n_{air} = 1$
   So, $n_{diamond} = \sin\theta_1/\sin\theta_2$ *[1 mark]*
   $\sin\theta_2 = \sin 50/2.419... = 0.316...$
   $\theta_2 = \sin^{-1}(0.316...) = 18.459... = $ **18.5° (to 3 s.f.)** *[1 mark]*
   You can assume the refractive index of air is 1, and don't forget to write the
   degree sign in your answer.

2 a) When the light is pointing steeply upwards some of it is refracted
   and some reflected — the beam emerging from the surface is the
   refracted part *[1 mark]*.
   However when the beam hits the surface at more than the critical
   angle (to the normal to the boundary) refraction does not occur.
   All the beam is totally internally reflected to light the tank, hence
   its brightness *[1 mark]*.
   b) The critical angle is 90° − 41.25° = 48.75° *[1 mark]*.
   $n_{water} = 1/\sin C$
   $= 1/\sin 48.75°$
   $= 1/0.7518... = 1.3300... = $ **1.330 (to 4 s.f.)** *[1 mark]*
   The question talks about the angle between the light beam and the floor of
   the aquarium. This angle is 90° minus the incident angle — measured
   from a normal to the surface of the water.

Page 81 — Lenses

1 a) Rays meeting the lens parallel to the principal axis converge at the
   principle focus. *[1 mark]*
   b) $\frac{1}{v} = -\frac{1}{u} + \frac{1}{f}$ so $\frac{1}{v} = -\frac{1}{0.2} + \frac{1}{0.15} = \frac{5}{3}$ *[1 mark]*,
   so $v = \frac{3}{5} = $ **0.6 m** *[1 mark]*

2 a) $m = \frac{\text{size of image}}{\text{size of object}} = \frac{47.2}{12.5} = 3.776 = $ **3.78 (to 3 s.f.)** *[1 mark]*
   b) $m = \frac{v}{u}$, giving $v = m \times u$ *[1 mark]*
   $v = 3.776 \times 4.0 = 15.104 = $ **15 mm (to 2 s.f.)** *[1 mark]*
   c) $P = \frac{1}{f} = \frac{1}{u} + \frac{1}{v}$ *[1 mark]*, so $P = \frac{1}{0.004} + \frac{1}{0.015104} = 316.20...$
   = **320 D (to 2 s.f.)** *[1 mark]*
   d) $P_{total} = \frac{1}{f} = \frac{1}{0.0022} = 454.5...$ D *[1 mark]*
   Rearrange $P_{total} = P_1 + P_2$ to give:
   $P_2 = P_{total} - P_1 = 454.5... - 316.20... = 138.33...$
   = **140 D (to 2 s.f.)** *[1 mark]*

Answers

Page 83 – Diffraction

1   When a wavefront meets an obstacle, the waves will diffract round the corners of the obstacle. When the obstacle is much bigger than the wavelength, little diffraction occurs. In this case, the mountain is much bigger than the wavelength of short-wave radio. So the "shadow" where you cannot pick up short wave is very long *[1 mark]*.

[1 mark]

When the obstacle is comparable in size to the wavelength, as it is for the long-wave radio waves, more diffraction occurs. The wavefront re-forms after a shorter distance, leaving a shorter "shadow" *[1 mark]*.

2   E.g. Set up a ripple tank, using an oscillating paddle to create straight, parallel waves. Place two objects into the water, creating a barrier with a gap in the middle *[1 mark]*. Vary the sizes of the objects to increase and decrease the gap width. Observe the amount of diffraction of the water waves as the gap width varies *[1 mark]*. The most diffraction will be seen when the gap is roughly the same size as the wavelength of the water waves *[1 mark]*.

Page 85 – Diffraction Gratings

1 a) Use $\sin \theta = n\lambda / d$
For the first order, $n = 1$
So, $\sin \theta = \lambda / d$ *[1 mark]*
No need to actually work out d. The number of lines per metre is 1 / d. So you can simply multiply the wavelength by that.
$\sin \theta = 6.00 \times 10^{-7} \times 4.0 \times 10^5 = 0.24$
$\theta = \sin^{-1}(0.24) = 13.8865... = \mathbf{14° \ (to \ 2 \ s.f.)} \ [1 \ mark]$
For the second order, $n = 2$ and $\sin \theta = 2\lambda / d$. *[1 mark]*
You already have a value for λ / d. Just double it to get $\sin \theta$ for the second order.
$\sin \theta = 0.48$
$\theta = \sin^{-1}(0.48) = 28.685... = \mathbf{29° \ (to \ 2 \ s.f.)} \ [1 \ mark]$

b) No. Putting $n = 5$ into the equation gives a value of $\sin \theta$ of 1.2, which is impossible *[1 mark]*.

2   $\sin \theta = n\lambda / d$, so for the 1st order maximum, $\sin \theta = \lambda / d$
$\sin 14.2° = \lambda \times 3.70 \times 10^5$ *[1 mark]*
$\lambda = \mathbf{663 \ nm \ (or \ 6.63 \times 10^{-7} \ m) \ (to \ 3 \ s.f.)} \ [1 \ mark].$

Page 87 – Light – Wave or Photon?

1 a) i) $E \ (eV) = V = 12.1 \ eV$ *[1 mark]*
ii) $E \ (J) = E \ (eV) \times (1.60 \times 10^{-19}) = 12.1 \times (1.60 \times 10^{-19})$
$= \mathbf{1.94 \times 10^{-18} \ J \ (to \ 3 \ s.f.)} \ [1 \ mark]$

b) i)   The movement of an electron from a lower energy level to a higher energy level by absorbing energy *[1 mark]*.
ii) $-13.6 + 12.1 = -1.5 \ eV$. This corresponds to $n = 3$ *[1 mark]*.
iii) $n = 3 \rightarrow n = 2$: $-1.5 - (-3.4) = \mathbf{1.9 \ eV}$ *[1 mark]*

$E = hf$, so $f = \dfrac{E}{h} = \dfrac{1.9 \times 1.60 \times 10^{-19}}{6.63 \times 10^{-34}} = 4.5852... \times 10^{14} \ Hz$
$= \mathbf{4.6 \times 10^{14} \ Hz \ (to \ 2 \ s.f.)} \ [1 \ mark]$
$n = 2 \rightarrow n = 1$: $-3.4 - (-13.6) = 10.2 \ eV$
$= \mathbf{10 \ eV \ (to \ 2 \ s.f.)} \ [1 \ mark]$

$f = \dfrac{E}{h} = \dfrac{10.2 \times 1.60 \times 10^{-19}}{6.63 \times 10^{-34}}$
$= 2.4615... \times 10^{15} \ Hz$
$= \mathbf{2.5 \times 10^{15} \ Hz \ (to \ 2 \ s.f.)} \ [1 \ mark]$
$n = 3 \rightarrow n = 1$: $-1.5 - (-13.6) = 12.1$
$= \mathbf{12 \ eV \ (to \ 2 \ s.f.)} \ [1 \ mark]$

$f = \dfrac{E}{h} = \dfrac{12.1 \times 1.60 \times 10^{-19}}{6.63 \times 10^{-34}}$
$= 2.9200... \times 10^{15} \ Hz$
$= \mathbf{2.9 \times 10^{15} \ Hz \ (to \ 2 \ s.f.)} \ [1 \ mark]$

Page 89 – The Photoelectric Effect

1   $\phi = 2.9 \ eV = 2.9 \times (1.60 \times 10^{-19}) \ J = 4.64 \times 10^{-19} \ J$ *[1 mark]*
$f = \dfrac{\phi}{h} = \dfrac{4.64 \times 10^{-19}}{6.63 \times 10^{-34}} = 6.99... \times 10^{14}$
$= \mathbf{7.0 \times 10^{14} \ Hz \ (to \ 2 \ s.f.)} \ [1 \ mark]$

2 a) $E = hf$
$= (6.63 \times 10^{-34}) \times (2.0 \times 10^{15}) = 1.326 \times 10^{-18} \ J$ *[1 mark]*
$1.326 \times 10^{-18} \ J = \dfrac{1.326 \times 10^{-18}}{1.60 \times 10^{-19}} \ eV$
$= 8.2875 = \mathbf{8.3 \ eV \ (to \ 2 \ s.f.)} \ [1 \ mark]$

b) $hf = \phi + \frac{1}{2}mv^2$, where $\frac{1}{2}mv^2$ is the maximum kinetic energy, so this can rearranged to give:
$E_{k \ (max)} = hf - \phi$
$= 8.2875 - 4.7 = 3.5875$ *[1 mark]*
$= \mathbf{3.6 \ eV \ (to \ 2 \ s.f.)} \ (or \ 5.7 \times 10^{-19} \ J \ to \ 2 \ s.f.) \ [1 \ mark]$

3   An electron needs to gain a certain amount of energy (the work function energy) from one photon before it can leave the surface of the metal *[1 mark]*.
If the energy carried by each photon is less than this work function energy, no electrons will be emitted *[1 mark]*.

Page 91 – Wave-Particle Duality

1 a) Electromagnetic radiation can show characteristics of both particles and waves *[1 mark]*.

b) $\lambda = \dfrac{h}{p}$
so $p = \dfrac{h}{\lambda}$ *[1 mark]*
$= \dfrac{6.63 \times 10^{-34}}{590 \times 10^{-9}} = 1.123... \times 10^{-27}$
$= \mathbf{1.1 \times 10^{-27} \ kg \, ms^{-1} \ (to \ 2 \ s.f.)} \ [1 \ mark]$

2 a) $\lambda = \dfrac{h}{p} = \dfrac{h}{mv}$
$\lambda = \dfrac{6.63 \times 10^{-34}}{9.11 \times 10^{-31} \times 3.50 \times 10^6}$ *[1 mark]*
$= 2.079... \times 10^{-10}$
$= \mathbf{2.08 \times 10^{-10} \ m \ (to \ 3 \ s.f.)} \ [1 \ mark]$

b) Either $\lambda = \dfrac{h}{p} = \dfrac{h}{mv}$
So $v = \dfrac{h}{m\lambda} = \dfrac{6.63 \times 10^{-34}}{1.673 \times 10^{-27} \times 2.079... \times 10^{-10}}$ *[1 mark]*
$= 1905.85... = \mathbf{1910 \ ms^{-1} \ (to \ 3 \ s.f.)} \ [1 \ mark]$
Or momentum of protons = momentum of electrons
so $m_p \times v_p = m_e \times v_e$
$v_p = v_e \times \dfrac{m_e}{m_p} = 3.50 \times 10^6 \times \dfrac{9.11 \times 10^{-31}}{1.673 \times 10^{-27}}$ *[1 mark]*
$= 1905.85... = \mathbf{1910 \ ms^{-1} \ (to \ 3 \ s.f.)} \ [1 \ mark]$

c) The proton has a larger mass, so it will have a smaller speed, since the two have the same kinetic energy *[1 mark]*. Kinetic energy is proportional to the square of the speed, while momentum is proportional to the speed, so they will have different momenta *[1 mark]*. Wavelength depends on the momentum, so the wavelengths are different *[1 mark]*.
This is a really hard question. If you didn't get it right, make sure you understand the answer fully. Do the algebra if it helps.

3   **B** *[1 mark]*

Index

Index

Index